BURT FRANKLIN: RESEARCH & SOURCE WORKS SERIES 497
Selected Essays in History, Economics, & Social Science 142

A CONCISE HISTORY

OF THE

IRON MANUFACTURE

OF THE

AMERICAN COLONIES

OLD FURNACE ON THE CONEMAUGH.

A CONCISE HISTORY

OF THE

IRON MANUFACTURE

OF THE

AMERICAN COLONIES

UP TO THE REVOLUTION,

AND OF

PENNSYLVANIA

UNTIL THE PRESENT TIME.

———————

BY JOHN B. PEARSE, A. M.,

METALLURGIST, ENGINEER, COMMISSIONER OF GEOLOGICAL SURVEY OF
PENNSYLVANIA, &C.

———————

BURT FRANKLIN
NEW YORK

Published by BURT FRANKLIN
235 East 44th St., New York, N.Y. 10017
Originally Published: 1876
Reprinted: 1970
Printed in the U.S.A.

Library of Congress Card Catalog No.: 72-125890
Burt Franklin: Research and Source Works Series 497
Selected Essays in History, Economics, and Social Science 142

PREFACE.

T HE following historical essay will, it is believed, be found
to contain most that is of interest concerning the early
manufacture of iron in North America. It is the result of a long
search, and embodies in succinct form nearly all the matter at
present accessible. The author hopes that its publication at this
time may bring to light additional facts, and that in the future
he may have an opportunity to complete the work so as to
include all the States as thoroughly as Pennsylvania. So far
as concerns Pennsylvania, the work is complete in its present
form, from the inception of the iron trade till the present time.

JOHN B. PEARSE.

IRON MANUFACTURE IN AMERICA.

THE American colonies were originally settled for the purposes of trade, the portion settled by exiles for the sake of religious opinions being confined to Massachusetts. It thus happened that iron, so necessary a material to the early colonists, occupied a most important place in the schemes of the early trading companies. And this occurred, not only through the needs of the colonies, but on account of the dearness of iron in Great Britain and the scarcity of wood.

So early as 1557 it was forbidden to use timber trees of oak, beech, or ash for charcoal; and in 1584 the erection of iron-works was unlawful in Sussex, Surrey, and Kent, except on freehold grounds on which forests had been replanted. The "voracious iron-works," however, driven thence, devoured the northern forests so that White, of Nottingham, wrote:—"The forests were consumed in melting the ore by a kind of foot-blast, before the introduction of better engines, and the workmen frequently shifted their ground, as the wood or ore decreased, till they had overrun the whole country." Evelyn says:—"Certainly, the goodly rivers and forests of the other world (America) would much better become our iron and saw mills than these exhausted countries."

VIRGINIA.

The first iron made in this country was made in Virginia. Captain John Smith early called attention to the iron-ore of Virginia, and Sir Thomas Gates (1610) mentioned "iron-ore ten miles in circuit, of which we have made trial at home; that it makes as good iron as any in Europe." In April, 1608, ore was sent from Jamestown to England, and was smelted in the autumn, yielding seventeen tons of pig metal, which was sold to the East India Company for four pounds sterling per ton.

Sir Edwin Sandys (1620) says, that one hundred and ten iron-workers from Warwickshire and Staffordshire, and forty from Sussex, were sent to Virginia to erect three iron-works. A letter of the Virginia Company to Jamestown, in 1621, says, "the advancement of the iron-works we esteem to be most necessary." Mr. John Berkely was sent out to locate and erect iron-works and saw-mills for the shipwrights of the company. The works were finally built at Falling creek, on the west bank of the James river, sixty-six miles above "James Citie," or about eight miles below the present site of Richmond, according to Fry & Jefferson's map. Mr. Berkely certified "that a more fit place for iron-works was not to be found for woods, water, mines, and stone, and that by Whitsuntide next (1622) iron would be made." Mr. George Sandis (March 3d, 1621) confirms this, with the remark that "Falling creek was so fitted for the purpose, as if nature had applied herself to the wish and direction of the workmen."

But, alas! in 1622 (March 22d), Mr. John Berkely, "with twenty-two men, two women, and three children," were massacred by the Indians, and the works destroyed before they got into the body of the mines. (Beverley.)

The iron proved reasonably good. Maurice Barkley was directed to employ the survivors and rebuild the works; but in 1624 the Virginia Company was dissolved by royal decree, and the whole enterprise fell to the ground.

Sir Thomas Glover wrote to the Royal Society, before 1670, as follows:—"The Cliffs of all the rivers (of Virginia) are full of great veins of iron-mine, and in some places of the country I have seen rocks of the same kind a foot above the earth; and generally all the highlands under the mould are a mere Rock of Iron. But an Iron-work would cost £3000, and the country being generally poor, they were discouraged from running the mineral by reason of the charge, tho' I believe the true reason is, their being so intent on their Tobacco Plantations, that they neglect all other more noble and advantageous improvements."

It is interesting to note that the Assembly of the Colony, in order to encourage the manufacture, forbade, in 1662 and again in 1682, the exportation of iron from Virginia, under a penalty of ten pounds of tobacco for each pound exported.

Williams (Virginia, 1650) says:—"Forty (40) servants will, by their labor, raise to the adventurer four thousand pounds yearly." * * * "Neither does Virginia yield to any other Province whatsoever in excellency and plenty of this ore; and I cannot promise to myself any other than extraordinary success and gain if that noble and useful staple be but vigorously followed. And indeed it had long ere this grown to a full perfection, if the treachery of the Indians had not crushed it in the beginning, and the backwardness of the Virginia merchants to re-erect it hindered that country from the benefit arising from that universal staple."

The general descriptions quoted above apply also to Maryland, for in those days the term, "Colony of Virginia," had a very wide significance, and included territory contiguous to Massachusetts bay.

Alexander names 1715 as the epoch of furnaces in Virginia, Maryland, and Pennsylvania; while Karsten fixes 1730 as the date. But it is probable that 1724 is the true date of the erection of furnaces, because the first furnaces in the southern colonies were built by Colonel Alexander Spotswood, "above the falls of the Rappahannock," as stated by Hugh Jones (1724) in his "Present Condition of Virginia." Further, we find that though the first bar iron was exported to Great Britain in 1718, no export of pig iron took place till 1729. Colonel Spotswood was a soldier of great ability, skilled in mathematics, architecture, and engineering, who was governor of Virginia from 1710 till 1723. After that date he devoted himself to iron-making. Major Gouge, his successor, paid great attention to the development of iron manufacture, and so did Sir William Keith, another governor, to whom, as we shall further see, Pennsylvania is indebted for its first furnace.

We are enabled to fix the date of the early southern furnaces definitely by the statements of Joseph Farmer, a steelmaker of Birmingham, who testified, in 1736, before a Parliamentary committee. He had tried, he said, the Potomac iron, but found it too tender, though fit for ordinary uses. Pennsylvania iron he had tried in every form but steel, and found it entirely fit for all purposes. He said, further, he had been in the Plantations, in 1718 and 1719, with the view of trying the ore there. During his stay he examined various localities and ores, finding good ore of all sorts, but the very best on the south side of Virginia. *At that time, he stated, there were no furnaces nor forges, but only two bloomeries, where they made iron for their own use only.*

Colonel William Byrd, of Westover, a very able man, being desirous of improving his own property, journeyed, in 1732, through the "Northern Neck," the long peninsula between the Potomac and Rappahannock rivers. This peninsula was then the principal seat of the iron manufacture, there being in it, in 1732, four blast-furnaces, but no forge.

Byrd says, in his "Progress to the Mines":—"I let him (Colonel Spotswood) understand that, beside the pleasure of paying him a visit, I came to be instructed by so great a master in the mystery of making iron, wherein he led the way, and was the Tubal Cain of Virginia. He corrected me a little there, by assuring me that he was *not only the first in this country but the first in North America* who had erected a regular furnace. That they ran altogether as bloomeries in New England and Pennsylvania, till his example had made them attempt greater works. But in Pennsylvania they have so few ships to carry their iron to Great Britain, that they must be content to make it only for their own use, and must be obliged to manufacture it when done."

Two furnaces belonged to Colonel Spotswood, who was in partnership with Robert Cary, of England. The firm built the *first air furnace* in the country (at Massaponux), and claimed the ability to furnish castings at twenty shillings per ton. It was built of stone and lined with Stourbridge brick. The furnaces were apparently located at Germanna, in Culpepper county, on the right bank of the Rapidan, and at Spotswood, in Spotsylvania county, seven miles below Fredericksburg, on the left bank of the Rapidan. Another furnace was near

Fredericksville, Culpepper county, and belonged to a company composed of Captain Pearse, Dr. Nicolas, Mr. Chiswell, Mr. Nelson, and the Governor. Mr. Chiswell was manager, receiving £100 yearly; and one-fifth interest in the company sold for £500. The fourth furnace belonged to Mr. England, Augustine Washington (father of General George Washington), and others. It was situated on the north side of the Rappahannock, in King George county, on the lands of Augustine Washington. Mr. Washington mined and delivered the ore, hauling it two miles to the furnace, for twenty shillings per ton of iron made. Colonel Spotswood and Mr. Chiswell agreed on the following statements, which afford a clear picture of the iron business at that time:—

For one moderate furnace four square miles of woodland and one hundred to one hundred and twenty slaves were required. One furnace cost £700, ready for work; Mr. Chiswell's property cost £12,000, including one furnace, fifteen thousand acres of land, the necessary cattle, eighty negroes, and the expense of making one thousand two hundred tons of pig iron.

Wood cut, mauled, cut to length (four feet), and delivered at pits for two shillings per cord. Charcoal coaled at five shillings per load of one hundred and sixty bushels.

Limestone brought from Bristol, England, as ballast, at two and one-half shillings per ton. The founders would not use oyster-shells.

One furnace used four hundred loads or six thousand four hundred bushels of charcoal in three months, and by good luck, with honest colliers and foremen, produced eight hundred tons per annum, at the rate of about twenty tons per week.

The founder got four shillings per ton of sow iron run out, or he got three and one-half shillings and his provisions.

The people to be hired were the founder, miner, collier, stock-taker, clerk, smith, carpenter, wheelwright, and several carters. These made, in all, a standing charge of £500 a year.

A good mason, who built Chiswell's furnace, received three and one-half shillings per day, reckoned from his departure from Gloucestershire till his return thither.

An English merchant, named Harrison, controlled the Virginia trade, so that American pig sold for six pounds sterling, while English pig brought from seven to eight pounds sterling per ton.

The charges on pig iron exported to England were—freight, seven and one-half shillings; duties, three and three-quarter shillings, say eleven and one-half shilings in all. This sum was swelled to thirty shillings by merchants' charges for handling, storage, &c.; ten shillings was added for accidents, and the total expense amounted to two pounds sterling in all. The producer, therefore, had four pounds sterling, or, "it is to be hoped," at least three pounds sterling per ton of pig iron sent over.

Colonel Byrd states that the duty on bar iron was twenty-four shillings per ton, while it sold in England for ten pounds to sixteen pounds sterling per ton. English records show that the duty on bar iron was afterward two pounds one shilling and six fifteen one-hundredths pence sterling; and that in 1718 three tons seven hundred weight of bar iron were imported into England from Maryland.

Keith (Sir William), in his "History of Virginia," remarks that "there is no proposition in trade more demonstrable than that the British plantations in America, with very small encouragement, can afford any quantity of good iron, of equally good quality with that which is imported from the Baltic, Russia, and Spain, and at as cheap a rate as it comes from thence to be sold in England." English iron-masters acted on this view, for, in 1736, William Donne, of Bristol, stated to a committee of Parliament that he had two furnaces in Virginia and two slitting-mills in England, and that his men told him the Virginia iron was inclined to be cold short.

While the works on the coast were being thus built up, immigration was filling the great valley between the Blue Ridge and the main Appalachian chain. Brown hematite occurs in great profusion in the Lower Silurian limestone formations of the valley, and on this ore has been based the production of the region. The fact that the oldest furnaces were the northernmost seems to justify the inference that the manufacture in the Shenandoah valley was more closely allied with that of Pennsylvania than with the enterprises on the coast. It is a curious fact, however, that in this valley old English terms were used as late as 1856—red shire and cold shire for red short and cold short, and bar shire to denote iron good enough to be made into bars.

Zane's furnace, on Cedar creek, Frederick county, was "built before any iron-works in this region," and abandoned, with its forge, about 1828. The Pine forge, three and a half miles north of Newmarket, was built in 1725, rebuilt in 1835, and produced about fifty tons of bar iron yearly till the civil war. The Isabella furnace, on Hawksbill creek, a mile north of Luray, Page county, was built in 1760, and abandoned in 1841. The Mossy creek furnace, on the headwaters of the south branch of the Shenandoah, in Augusta county, fourteen miles north-west of Staunton, was built about 1760; its dimensions were about eight and a half feet across the boshes by twenty-eight feet high. It was burnt in 1841, and in 1856 lay a ruin, surrounded in every direction by old ore-banks. The Mossy creek forge, a mile from the furnace, was built about 1757, rebuilt in 1767 and again in 1836; it made about seventy-five tons of bars yearly till the war. In 1856 it used twenty-eight to twenty-nine hundred weight of pig to the ton of bar iron. The longevity of these forges in the valley is due to the fact that they made a small production without competition, solely for the use of a rich farming region.

The great valley south of James River Gap also contained several iron-works before the Revolution. Jefferson thus describes the production of Virginia in 1781, in his "Notes on Virginia":—

"The mines of iron worked at present are Callaway's, Ross', and Ballandine's, on the south side of James river; Old's on the north side in Albemarle; Miller's in Augusta, and Zane's in Frederick. These two last are in the valley between the Blue Ridge and the North Mountain. Callaway's, Ross', Miller's, and Zane's make about one hundred and fifty tons of bar iron each in the year; Ross' makes also about sixteen hundred tons of pig iron annually; Ballandine's a thousand; Callaway's, Miller's, and Zane's about six hundred each. Besides these a forge of Mr. Hunter's, at Fredericksburg, makes about three hundred tons a year of bar iron *from pigs imported from Maryland;* and Taylor's forge on Neapsco of Potomac works the same way, but to what extent I am not informed. The undertakers of iron in other places are numerous and dispersed through all the middle country. The toughness of the cast iron of Ross' and Zane's furnaces is remarkable. Pots and other utensils cast thinner than usual of this iron may be safely thrown into or out of the wagons in which they are transported. Salt-pans made of the same, and no longer wanted for that purpose, cannot be broken up in order to be melted again, unless previously drilled in many parts."

Ross' works were probably those on Beaver creek, near Lynchburg, named, in 1856, "Oxford," but once known as the "Old Davie Ross furnace." The location of the other works is uncertain.

MARYLAND.

In Maryland, the first forge was built in 1717, at "Principio, at the head of the bay," by England and Washington, with English partners. Very good bar iron was made there, and a furnace was afterwards added. Emanuel Swedenborg thus describes the Principio works, in 1734:—"The principal works is called Principio, in the upper part of the province of Maryland, on the river Principio. The ore is dug fifty miles away, and is brought to the works in vessels with two banks of oars, and on boats. The ore is said to be of a gray or yellowish color, not unlike Holland pottery-ware, and contains fifty per cent. of iron. The iron from this ore is said to excel all others."

While the Virginia works used slave labor, with English or German foremen (Spotswood's men were German), the Maryland furnaces, especially in later years, used either indented English convicts or redemptioners, whose labor was sold for a term of years.

Maryland made remarkable progress before the Revolution, owing to legislative encouragement of the iron manufacture. Under acts of Assembly of 1719, chapter 15; 1732, chapter 7, and 1736, chapter 17, no less than twenty-three charters were taken out for iron-works between 1733 and 1767. These acts are yet unrepealed, though inoperative since 1776. They related to the extinguishment of the rights of the Lord Proprietary to royalty on minerals, and allowed a hundred acres to be taken for each iron-works at assessed damages. Workmen at furnaces and forges were also exempted from labor on roads. The chief existing records, however, of the early Maryland furnaces, are the sheriff's advertisements exposing them for sale, the period from 1765 to 1770 having proved very disastrous. The earliest furnaces and forges were located in Cecil, Baltimore, Anne Arundel, Queen Anne, and Somerset counties, and the Carrols, Dulanys, and Taskers were the principal early iron-masters of Maryland.

The excellent spathic ores of the tertiary clays and sands along the west coast of Chesapeake bay attracted attention at a very early date. Plantagenet, in his "New Albion," written in 1648, points out the facility of the water-carriage at hand and the readiness with which the ore might be mined. He estimates the saving in these items at three pounds sterling per ton of iron, valued then at twelve pounds sterling per ton. He thought that five pounds sterling more could be saved in the item of fuel by using drift timber brought down by the rivers.

The earliest works, however, were the forge Principio, described above; it began as a bloomery, but was afterward run as a finery forge (*i.e.*, using pig iron). A furnace was afterward erected at Principio, near the site of the present Principio furnace. Alexander mentions part of the old stack as still standing in 1840. The forge at North-east was probably built about the same time, as one hundred acres were pre-empted by John Rushton, on North-east river, in 1734, and assigned afterward to William Chetwynd, of Surrey, England. In Harford county the Bush furnace and Onion's furnace, a mile from Joppa, were for sale in 1767 and 1769, respectively. In Baltimore, which included Harford county, the earliest furnace and one of the first in the region was one erected before 1733 by B. Tasker, C. Carrol, D. Dulany, Dr. C. Carrol, and D. Carrol, of Duddington, under the name of the Baltimore Company, for which one hundred acres were pre-empted on Charles branch and Gwin's falls. The Hampton or Northampton furnace was built in 1760 by John and Charles Ridgely, who ran also the Long Cam forge on the Great Gunpowder; this forge antedated the furnace, which stood ten miles west of Baltimore. Cannon were cast at it in 1780. On Stemmer's run, seven miles from Baltimore City, stood a furnace; the Kingsbury furnace was on Herring run, and on Jones' falls, near the city, lay the Mount Royal forge. In Anne Arundel county Edward Dorsey owned the Elkridge furnace and forge at Elkridge Landing, on the Patapsco. Mr. Dorsey also owned a rolling and slitting mill on the Patapsco, near the site occupied afterwards by the Avalon Iron-Works. The former were stopped in 1750 by act of Parliament. The Patuxent furnace and forge were built by Thomas, Richard, and Edward Snowden. Old Hampton furnace, on Tom's creek, west of Emmetsburg, was built about 1760, and Legh furnace, on Little Pipe creek, south-west of Westminster, was built by Legh Master, an Englishman, about the same time; both were abandoned in a

few years for want of ore. All these had been abandoned before 1840.

Ten or fifteen years before the Revolution iron-making
began in Frederic county and in Washington county
in 1770. This beginning was due to the energy of
James, Roger, Thomas, and Baker Johnson, who made
up the firm, "James Johnson & Co." The old Catoctin
furnace, about twelve miles north-west of Frederic, was
built in 1774 by the Johnsons and rebuilt in 1787, about
three-fourths of a mile up Little Hunting creek, nearer
the ore-banks. It left the hands of the firm in 1793,
and was abandoned 1840. It was rebuilt, however, and
is still running.

The yield of the old Catoctin furnace was stated to
have been twelve to eighteen tons per week from brown
hematite ore, containing in its cavities more or less
phosphate of iron and also carbonate of zinc. In 1775
Johnson & Co. built a forge on Bush creek, consisting
of a "finery and a chafery," which made three to four
tons of iron per week. The Baltimore and Ohio
Railroad now passes directly over the site of the
hammer-wheel, the forge having been abandoned in
1810. The firm also erected the Johnson furnace, a
mile above the mouth of the Monocacy; it made twelve
to fifteen tons a week out of ore from Point of Rocks.
This furnace also had a finery and chafery, which afterward worked up "*stamp-stuff* from the cinder-heaps
of old Catoctin." These were abandoned about 1800.
Fielderea furnace, near Frederic, on the south, made
one blast only before 1790.

In Washington county the Johnsons built Green
Spring furnace on Green Spring run, and Licking
creek forge on Licking creek. The furnace was soon
abandoned, and the forge sold to Mr. Chambers, of

Chambersburg, Pennsylvania. Samuel and Daniel Hughes built the Mount Ætna furnace on a branch of the Antietam, north of Hagerstown; it cast *cannon* during the Revolution, which failed at first, but afterwards acquired such credit that Congress advanced eight thousand dollars on a contract for one thousand tons of cannon, to be delivered in a year. Nearer Hagerstown the old Antietam forge drew its iron from the furnace, but after the latter stopped it used Pennsylvania iron. The present Antietam Works were built by Henderson & Ross, in 1775.

McMahon (History of Maryland) states, apparently, that there were in 1749 eight furnaces and nine forges in operation, and in the council proceedings of August 23d, 1756, the same number is reported to the British Commissioners of Trade and Plantations. A similar report, made December 21st, 1761, shows eight furnaces, making about two thousand five hundred tons of pig iron, and ten forges capable of making six hundred tons of bar iron.

A statement laid before Parliament in 1749, by Mrs. Crowley & Co., gives the following information:—There were in Virginia and Maryland (say 1749) ten blast-furnaces at work, which made, one year with another, five hundred tons each per year, or a total of five thousand tons of pig iron. In 1735 Mrs. Crowley & Co. received and sold twenty-five tons of Maryland bar iron to government dock-yards, receiving very favorable reports. In 1746 a further lot of twenty-five tons was sold by the same firm for fourteen to sixteen pounds sterling per ton, and when slit into rods for eighteen pounds sterling per ton. The same firm imported, from 1744 to 1746, Maryland bar into London, selling it at thirteen pounds ten shillings to fifteen pounds sterling

per ton. The manufacturers to whom it was sold
reported it "in no way inferior to Swedish iron, and it
could very properly and usefully be substituted therefor."
John Gopsill used both Swedish and American iron in
making shovels and spades for the government, and
while he often gave large prices for Swedish bar iron,
of which fifty per cent. proved waste, he had found
that he did not throw aside more than ten per cent. of
the American bar. Mr. Ed. Knight testified before
Parliament (1750) that he had been conversant with
the different kinds of pig made by the Bristol Company (William Donne), two furnaces in Virginia, the
Potomac, Tubal, the Pennsylvania, and the "N. B. &
F." (exactly F. C. N. B.), all American, all which were
cold short and chiefly fit for making nails. He said,
however, "that the Baltimore and Principio were the
best sort of American iron, and were of a kind, malleable nature, and generally softer than any English iron,
except that made from Cumberland ore." John Bannister testified that bar iron, made from Baltimore and
Principio pigs, which were worth from six pounds to
six pounds ten shillings sterling per ton, cost Mrs.
Crowley fifteen pounds sterling per ton; and that a
load and a half of coal (charcoal), or three cords of
wood, were required as fuel for the conversion.

During twenty-four years, between 1729 and 1755
(excluding 1737, 1738, and 1739, for which no records
exist), Virginia and Maryland exported to Great Britain
fifty thousand nine hundred and fifty-eight seventy
one-hundredths tons of pig iron, and nine hundred
and seventy-five thirteen one-hundredths tons of bar
iron,—an average of two thousand one hundred and
twenty-three and eleven one-hundredths tons of pig
exported yearly.

MASSACHUSETTS.

Notwithstanding the early progress of Virginia, the colony of Massachusetts Bay was neither idle nor far behind Virginia in making iron. Virginia made, indeed, the first iron, but very little of it, and the attempt was abandoned before Massachusetts began. The record of the latter colony, though irregular, is more or less continuous from 1629 to the present day.

In 1629 Mr. Malbon was commissioned to examine New England, "with reference to iron-works and the formation of a Company of Undertakers." The first iron-works in Massachusetts was that at Lynn, mentioned in the records of the "Sixth Church of Christ, held at Linn, 1631," as follows:—"This town is furnished with minerals of divers kinds, especially iron and lead. * * * Here is also an iron-mill in constant use." In 1643 the second works—a blast-furnace—were started at Hammersmith, on the west bank of the Saugus river, by Thomas Dexter and Robert Bridges, with some success. Bridges soon went to London with specimens of bog ore, and formed a "Company of Undertakers for Iron-works," consisting of Messrs. Copley, Bond, Pury, Becx, Beauchamp, Foley, Greenhill, Weld, Pococke, Becke, and Hicocke, with whom John Winthrop, Jr., a son of Governor Winthrop, was interested from the first. In 1644 this company was formally incorporated by the General Court, with the following privileges:—

A monopoly of twenty-one years, and all persons to have liberty to join till the end of first month, on subscribing one hundred pounds sterling, provided, after two years, enough iron be made for the country's use.

Waste and other lands granted, provided not more than six places are taken up, and within ten years *an iron furnace and forge, and not a bloomery only*, be set up at each place. Three miles square (five thousand seven hundred and sixty acres) were allotted to each place or works.

Undertakers to have three years for perfecting their works, provided the adventurers prosecute the good work to perfection, as well the finery and forge as *the blast-furnace, which is already started*, so that the country be furnished with all sorts of bar iron, under twenty pounds sterling per ton.

Undertakers, associates, and servants to be free from taxation for twenty years for any stock in this adventure, and be free from training.

In 1645 (14th May) the General Court passed the following resolutions:—

"WHEREAS, It is now found, by sufficient proof, that the iron-works is successful, both in richness of ore and goodness of iron;

"AND WHEREAS, The time set for limit expires the ninth of next month, and the work is of great benefit, *all citizens are requested to take stock according to their ability*, and to know that £1200 to £1500 have already been spent, with which the furnace is built, with its belongings, and good quantity of mine, coal, and wood provided, and some tons of iron cast, and other things in readiness for the forge, &c.; and there will be need of some £1500 to finish the forge. This is to be paid in to Henry Webbe, of Boston, John Winthrop, Jr., Major Sedgwick, and Josua Hewes."

In 1645, also, a formal agreement, in accordance with the above charter, was made between the colony and the Undertakers, who received these additional privileges:—

As many works as convenient may be put in one place, still retaining the allowance of three miles square to each.

A general permission to use all dams, sluices, watercourses, and ponds.

Undertakers can sell iron to all persons, not excluding Indians or enemies.

There seem to have been two companies, the one at Lynn, previously mentioned, and the other that of Bridges and Winthrop. The latter established works at Hammersmith, Braintree, and Raynham, now Taunton. These works were erected and managed by a family of Leonards, who came from Pontypool, in Monmouthshire, and were remarkable for longevity and promotion to office. James and Henry Leonard were at Hammersmith in 1642, at Braintree in 1646, at Raynham in 1652, where they are reported to have built the *first forge* in America, and at Rowley village in 1668. In 1652 Henry went to New Jersey, where he was one of the first to set up iron-works. In Massachusetts the proverb took root, "where you can find an iron-works you will find a Leonard." Rev. Dr. Fobes, in his history of Raynham, written in 1793, states that "the first adventurers from England to this country who were skilled in the forge-iron manufacture were two brothers, James and Henry Leonard. They came to this town in the year 1652, which was about two years after the first settlers had planted themselves upon this spot, and in the year 1652 these Leonards here built the first forge in America. * * * This forge was situated on the great road, and having been repaired from generation to generation, it is to this day still in employ."

From 1646 to 1657 the second company of Undertakers met prejudice and opposition, "because they
have been taking up all wood," and the citizens feared
a scarcity; because "they did not benefit the towns,
since they would only take money for their iron, and
the towns had little;" because the towns objected to
their freedom from taxes and flooding the country, and
instituted interminable lawsuits on the latter account;
because Giffard, their agent, was a rascal, "who mowed
forty acres of grass for six cattle only, made false
charges, sold some tons more iron than he credited,
was at vast expense, and made gifts," and defaulted for
£1300, including two accounts of one hundred and
eighty-nine tons bar iron, thirty-two tons rod iron, and
fifteen tons pots and cast-ware. Giffard's accounts were
declared false by the court, but the Undertakers were
nonsuited for failing to appear.

The Undertakers having exceeded the price of twenty
pounds sterling for bar iron, the towns of Concord and
Lancaster obtained, in 1657, permission to build iron-
works, which could be bought by the Undertakers within
one year, at a valuation. The General Court found it
necessary to encourage the industry, by enacting that
"whosoever shall transport any iron out of the government shall pay, unto the countrie's use, twelve pence on
every hundred, and he shall enter such iron, as he con-
veyeth or selleth away, with the town clarke, on penalty
of forfeiting one-third part of the value of it to the
countrie's use."

In 1671 the works at Hammersmith succumbed to
their embarrassments and were sold to Samuel Apple-
ton, who, in 1688, sold the whole to Thomas Taylor,
probably for their land (six hundred acres), since operations ceased about 1690. In regard to the Lynn

Works, Joselyn, in his "Second Voyage," 1663, mentions "one iron-works at Lynn." Concerning the other works no records have been preserved, and it is probable that they were broken up during King Philip's war, which began in 1675.

Timothy Hatherley, founder, of Scituate, obtained, in 1650, leave to erect an iron-mill, and took up ground for the purpose at Mattakeeset, now Pembroke. But nothing was done till 1702, when, on this precise grant, a furnace was erected by Mark Despard and the Barker family. Dr. Thatcher, writing in 1804, calls this the "first furnace" in Massachusetts, evidently without knowledge of the truth. This furnace, however, marked the commencement of the regular iron manufacture in the State. The earlier manufacture was tentative. The methods were original, and, like similar subsequent attempts, were failures. The citizens were interested as buyers, not manufacturers,—they would not become stockholders to their own disadvantage. The works were of no use, they said, if iron was sold for money only, since they had little money, and did not want that little sent to England. The people were jealous of the early privileges of the iron-works, and in one way or another, as we have seen, threw so many obstacles in their way that Hubbard wrote, "instead of drawing out bars of iron for the country's use, there was hammered out nothing but contentions and lawsuits." The royal commissioners reported in 1664 but one bloomery in Plymouth Colony; this was the forge at Raynham. In 1673, Edward Randolph reported to the commissioners, respecting New England, "There be five iron-works which cast no guns."

In the eighteenth century, however, affairs brightened, and the manufacture obtained a firm footing.

The efforts of the General Court were directed to the
increase of the bar iron product, and in 1718 the Council recommended and the Court passed a liberal bounty
bill, on the petition of Thomas Bardin, of Scituate, for
encouragement. The bill promised the following premiums for ten years:—Forty shillings sterling per ton
on bar iron equal to *Spanish*, provided the forge made
thirty tons annually—if more, sixty shillings per ton on
the excess; five pounds per ton on "rod iron or flaggots
of suitable thinness to work out rails;" twenty penny
per thousand 20d. nails and the same number of pence
premium per thousand as that denoting the grade of the
nails down to 3d. nails; twelve shillings on scythes
three feet nine inches long, if equal to the best imported
from Great Britain; forty shillings per ton on all cast-
iron hollow ware, if equal in quality to English or
Dutch ware. John Bannister testified (1738) that both
New England and Pennsylvania had manufactured iron
tools, &c. for many years, the drawback on wares
exported to the colonies having been taken off in 1711.
In 1722 one hundred and twenty *axes*, made at Boston,
were shipped to South Carolina. Captain Tomlinson,
who passed nine years in New England, about 1727–
1736, said that he had experimented on the Massachusetts iron and could see no difference between it and
Swedish. There was a slitting-mill in the colony, and
the iron-works made nails, axes, strakes for wagons,
&c. at about double English prices: they were, perhaps,
worth double, but at any rate found a ready sale,
which created a demand for bar iron and steel to make
them. The iron trade was still further strengthened
by the demand for arms and war material. We find it
recorded that, after the Revolution, in 1793, "the large
quantity of *coals* used for iron manufacture, in all its

branches, have greatly enhanced, within a few years, the value of wood, *and have occasioned emigration.*" Mass. Hist. Soc. Coll., 1st ser., iii., 167.

Douglass (I., 140) summarizes the iron trade of New England into "three branches:—(1.) Smelting-furnaces, reducing the ore into pigs, having coal (charcoal) enough and appearances of rock ore. In Attleborough were erected, at a great charge, three furnaces, but the ore proving bad and scarce, this projection miscarried as to pigs, but were of use in casting of small cannon for ships and letters of marque, and in casting cannon-balls and bombs for the (final) reduction of Louisburg (*note*, in 1745). (2.) Refineries, which manufactured pigs imported from New York, Pennsylvania, and Maryland furnaces into bar iron. (3.) Bloomeries, which, from bog or swamp ore, without any furnace, only by a forge hearth, reduce it into a bloom, or semi-liquified lump, to be beat into bars, but much inferior to those from pigs or refineries. (4.) Swamp-ore furnaces, from ore smelted they cast hollow ware, which we can afford cheaper than from England or from Holland."

We have not found many details regarding the early work, but the following facts are interesting:—In 1674, Nathaniel and Thomas Leonard, sons of James Leonard, built an iron-works at Rowley for John Ruck and others of Salem, but the bog ore was poor and the works failed. George Leonard erected iron-works about 1696 in Norton, utilizing the water-power of Taunton river. His descendants are yet in the trade in that vicinity. The Drinkwater Iron-works were built in 1710 on a large tract of land near Abington and Hanover, by a Mr. Mighill. This forge was running in 1865, as Curtis' Anchor forge, with eleven forge fires, one furnace, and four trip-hammers. A slitting-mill was run at Abington before the Revolution. The Bridgewater bloomery was built in 1691, and in 1750 we find a report to the governor of the province, from James and Abiel Packard, Daniel and David Haward, and Constant Southworth, its owners, that it was still running "in the North street, Bridgewater." Iron-works were erected in Plympton in 1730 by Joseph Thomas, which passed to Joseph Scot, and afterward to Mr. Beacham, both of Boston.

In March, 1739, Joseph Mallinson memorialized the General Court for a grant of land in consideration of being "the sole promoter" of the manufacture of hollow ware, cast in *sand moulds* instead of *clay moulds*. He obtained two hundred acres, though the justice of the claim is not apparent, in view of the facts that Joseph Jencks had made pots in 1646, and Jeremy Florio, an Englishman, was credited in Mallinson's time with the introduction of the process.

In 1747 a very rich deposit of ore was discovered in Assawampset pond, in Middleboro, and the Charlotte furnace, now abandoned, was built in the town in 1756. About this time, also, the Holmes forge was built in Plympton; its iron was well known during the Revolution, and it still exists as the Holmes Anchor forge. At Furnace village, in Hardwicke, Joseph Washbourne, of Braintree, built a furnace on the river Ware, and obtained a grant of a limestone-quarry site in Ashfield from the General Court. Springfield, on the Chicopee, was a central depot and manufacturing town for arms and munitions of war, during the Revolution, and in 1778 the Government works was founded on its present site and made a national armory in 1794, when the Harper's Ferry armory was built.

In Western Massachusetts iron-making began at a later date, owing to the isolated position of the mines of brown hematite ore. But their richness, purity, and the strength of the iron made from them, caused the erection of the Lenox furnace in 1765, built originally with one tuyere, but rebuilt in 1837 with three tuyeres, its dimensions being thirty-three feet high, and nine feet boshes, with a capacity of about one thousand six hundred tons a year. The furnaces in this part of the county now average about one hundred and forty-two bushels of charcoal to the ton of iron, using warm blast; with cold blast the average consumption was not less than two hundred bushels. In West Stockbridge, Pittsfield, and along the Housatonic, several furnaces were built during the last century, but, owing to the destruction of forests, were successively abandoned without special record. Timber was never cultivated nor preserved in those days, but now-a-days some attention is happily being directed to the subject.

In a report to a committee of Parliament, made about 1740, the governor of Massachusetts Bay said that "some iron-works had been in the province for many years, but the iron of Great Britain is esteemed best, and the iron-works of the province are not able to supply the twentieth part of the necessities of the province." In the returns made to the Lords of Trade, in 1750, we find that Massachusetts Bay had two slitting and rolling mills, one plating-forge, one steel-furnace, and one nail-works. The Surveyor of Her Majesty's woods reports shortly afterward six furnaces and nineteen forges for making iron. Tench Coxe, in his "View of the United States," says:—"There were in Massachusetts, in 1784, seventy-six iron-works, many of them small." After the Revolution, the production of bar iron made great progress in Massachusetts, for New England had taken most of the bar iron *imported* by the colonies. In 1795, Dr. Morse stated there were in three eastern counties of the State eleven mills; five in Bristol county, viz., three at Taunton, one at Pawtucket, one in Morton; four in Plymouth county, viz., two at Bridgewater, one at Plymouth, one at Kingston; two in Norfolk county, viz., one at Needham and one at Stoughton. They cut and rolled in 1795 one thousand seven hundred and thirty-two tons of iron; six hundred and ten tons were rolled for hoops, and the remainder for nail-rods. In 1804 there were (Thatcher) no Catalan forges at work "to any extent" in Massachusetts, but there were ten forges making about two hundred tons of bar iron per annum from old scrap, &c.

We append some interesting facts illustrative of early metallurgy in Massachusetts. Most of the iron of Eastern Massachusetts was made from bog ore dug in ponds. Doctor Fobes wrote, in 1793:—"There is a remarkable circumstance relating to this (Raynham) pond, viz., its property of generating ore. The beds are usually found near pine swamps or red soils, where the pine or cedar grow. If there is sufficient to filtrate the liquid mine before it is deposited in beds, there will be found a plenty of bog ore. The Raynham forge has been run for eighty years on a plenty of bog ore, though, like other things in a state of youth, it is weak and incapable of being wrought into iron of the best quality. *The subject promises a reward to investigation. The time may come when it will be as easy to raise a bed of bog ore as a bed of carrots.*"

Dr. Thatcher affords materials for the following description of the ores used in Massachusetts in the eighteenth century:—

The *bog ore* used was found in the vicinity of all ponds, especially where springs abound, and was not formed when the water was diverted. When dug it was usually formed again in seven to fifteen years, if the digger covered the hole with loose earth, leaves, and rubbish. Its color was rusty brown, its yield eighteen per cent., and it was worth four dollars per ton at the furnace.

The *pond ore* was got in ponds in (Brookfield, Raynham) Middleboro, Halifax, Carver, and Kingston. It was fished up from a depth of two to twenty-five feet with tongs, like oyster-dredges, and a man raised about half a ton per day. Its period of growth was believed to be twenty-five years, and it was supposed to be derived from the decomposition of a species of slate. There are three kinds—*Short ore*, reddish-brown lumps, the size of a bullet, yielding twenty-five per cent.; *pancake ore*, dark-brown ore, "in pieces like Turkey figs," yielding twenty-five to thirty per cent.; *black ore*, from a muddy bottom, in cakes; esteemed as a flux. The Middleboro pond yielded three hundred to six hundred tons a year for over sixty years. The average price of these ores at the furnace was six dollars per ton.

Upland ore was got from Martha's Vineyard in large lumps, yielding twenty-five per cent. The iron from this ore was "smooth, and has a high lustre."

"The Egg Harbor mines in New Jersey furnish large amounts of ore to our furnaces. This ore yields thirty to forty per cent. of excellent iron, and is usually calcined." Usual price was six dollars and a half per ton.

The ores were reduced in large furnaces of stone, with charcoal for fuel and oyster-shells as flux. The first furnace in Plymouth was built by Lambert (or Mark) Despard and the Barkers, his associates, in 1702, in the town of Pembroke, but the wood (1804) has long since been exhausted and the works abandoned. "Furnaces for pigs and furnaces for castings are not different,

but there are none of the former in Massàchusetts,
though ten of the latter in Plymouth county." The
furnaces were eight feet in diameter and twenty feet
high, and the interior resembled a "large hen's-egg
standing on its largest end." They were tapped every
nine or ten hours and one ton got at a cast. The blasts
did not usually exceed sixteen to eighteen weeks, and
two or three were made in six months, during which
time three hundred and sixty tons of hollow ware were
made. (*Hollow ware ton was one thousand two hundred
pounds.*)

Cost of Three Hundred and Sixty Tons of Hollow Ware.

Fifty loads, of eighty bushels each, are needed to heat furnace up.

Two thousand one hundred and thirty cords of wood burnt into one thousand four hundred and twenty loads of charcoal, at two dollars and fifty cents, . . .	$3,550 00
Seven hundred and twenty-six tons of ore, at six dollars, ...	4,356 00
Two sets of stone hearths, ...	153 32
Founders' pay at one dollar per ton, . .	360 00
Moulders' and workmen's wages, . .	2,331 00
	$10,750 32

This cost amounts to fifty-five dollars and seventy-five
cents per gross ton of hollow ware,—a very small cost,
considering that the ore used, except the Egg Harbor
ore, would now be considered worthless. The quantity
of hollow ware yearly made was estimated at one thousand five hundred tons per annum.

(Many men of ability were employed in these early
works; among others, Joseph Jenks, a machinist and

moulder, who made saws in 1652, and patterns for casting. One of the very first patents issued in America was granted him by the General Court "for ye making of engines for mills to goe with water, for ye more speedy dispatch of work than formerly, and mills for ye making of sithes and other edged tooles." The first pot cast in America was moulded from his patterns— a one-quart iron pot, cast in 1646 (?). He afterwards went to Rhode Island. At a later date (1738) Hugh Orr, a young Scotchman, came to Bridgewater from Renfrewshire. He erected a shop and the first trip-hammer known there. He was highly successful in the manufacture of scythes, and for several years was the only edge-tool maker in that part of the country. There was no branch of the iron trade in which his perseverance did not insure success. In 1748 he made the first arms produced in the colonies,—five hundred stand for the Province of Massachusetts Bay, and in his new foundry at Bridgewater he succeeded in casting cannon solid, boring them out with a boring-bar and cutter, followed by a reamer (Perkins' method). He made a large number of cannon during the Revolution. He possessed, too, great skill as a machinist, particularly in cotton machinery. He died in 1798, and his son Robert, master armorer at Springfield, made scythes under the trip-hammer by an improved method, and successfully introduced the shovel manufacture into Massachusetts.)

The Bridgewater forge, the oldest in the country, like several others of the early works, long ago ceased to make iron, except as aiding in the manufacture of forgings, shafts, anchors, &c. The Bridgewater Works, aided by the skill stored up in successive generations of workmen, and by the ingenuity of their owners, have built up the most important forge business in the country. Their work is based on scrap iron, which is carefully assorted and rolled into billets for large forgings, &c. They furnished, during the Rebellion, nearly our entire fleet, and also the Italian frigate "Re d'Italia," with screw-shafts and heavy iron work. They now have ten hammers, one of them a Nasmyth, with a tup weighing over eleven tons, and some of the heaviest machine-tools in the country. The present works were begun in 1785.

(We must not omit Jacob Perkins, who was born at Newburyport in 1766, and invented and set in operation, at Amesbury, about 1796, the first machine for cutting and heading nails, which could cut two hundred thousand nails a day. His subsequent career in Philadelphia and London placed him high among inventors, and he was most successful in the character and practical value of his designs, in all branches of mechanical engineering.)

RHODE ISLAND.

In regard to the early iron manufacture in Rhode Island I can find only the following letter of Roger Williams to John Winthrop, Jr., dated December 15th, 1654:—" Mr. Foote has once and again moved for iron-works at Providence. He told me you had speech with him about his getting of iron-men to Pequot, but he thought yourself would be more willing to promote the work, as well here as there, and therefore promised me to write to you. If I had power in my hand I would venture to such public good, and, however, shall gladly contribute all assistance, especially if your loving spirit and experience be pleased to give encouragement."

About this time, it may be in consequence of this letter, Joseph Jenks, above mentioned, left Hammersmith and built a forge at Pawtucket, which was destroyed in 1675, during the Wampanoag war with the Narragansett Indians.

The ore of Rhode Island, consisting of refractory magnetics and of iron sands on the coasts and neighboring islands, though early known, has never been extensively worked. The remarks of Douglass (quoted page 28), concerning Attleborough, now Cumberland, Rhode Island, show this. The deposits of ore, though extensive, are silicious and lean, not yielding over twenty to thirty per cent., according to General Leach, quoted by Professor Hitchcock. Samuel Waldo, who in 1735 built the Hope furnace and foundry on the Patuxent, in the town of Scituate, was more successful. He produced heavy castings, guns, shot, &c. before and during the Revolution.

Concerning the general trade of the province, Henry Calvert wrote, in 1737, "that in Rhode Island they make anchors of all sizes and export them to neighboring colonies. I hope before this time the Parliament has put a stop to their career of manufacturing, which both in that government, New England, and the Jerseys begins to increase vastly."

In a report to a committee of Parliament, about 1740, the governor of the colony said there were iron-mines in the colony which did not furnish one quarter of the iron required by the colony. After the Revolution there were two slitting-mills in the State,—one on the Providence river, and the manufactures of iron articles were quite extensive. No aid has, however, been derived from the anthracite coal of the State, which, though discovered in 1768, has never furnished much useful fuel, and is now only mined at Portsmouth for use in copper smelting.

CONNECTICUT.

The colony of Connecticut was in part founded for the sake of iron-works, though in its early days they never thrived. John Winthrop, Jr., after organizing a colony at the mouth of the Connecticut river, petitioned the General Court for leave to lay out a plantation and iron-works at Pequot, now New London, which was granted in 1644, and the works went into operation within three years.) Of these works Winthrop wrote, August 4th, 1648, "the furnace now yields seven tons per week out of brown earth under bog mine;" and on September 20th, "the furnace now runs eight tons per week, and their bar iron is as good as Spanish."

In 1651 the Assembly of the colony granted John Winthrop and his associates the right to the lands, wood, and water in the vicinity of any mines he might discover; and in 1655 the persons employed in and the capital of any iron-works which might be built were exempted from taxes and from attachment for individual debts of the proprietors.

Winthrop also built a blast furnace and forge at New Haven in 1657, in connection with William Paine, Thomas Clarke, John Davenport, and Mr. Goodyear. William Paine, who then owned the works at Hammersmith and a half interest in the works at Lynn and Braintree, built the forge, and urged Winthrop on Christmas, 1657, "to forward the work at New Haven, so that a blast may be made in the spring of the year." Singularly enough *this furnace used English ore*, for John Davenport wrote to Winthrop, in 1658:—" They are now, upon the failing of the stones sent by Mr. Goodyear, solicitous the work may not fail; and understanding that there are good stones at Quarry Hill, twenty miles from London, which are used at an iron-works four miles from that place, they are writing to Clarke and Paine to use their correspondents in London that these stones may be procured and sent over by the first ship in the spring. Mr. Goodyear says they may be bought for one pound sterling per ton, which is far below what the merchant at Milford demands for bringing stones from the Isle of Wight."

Of this works Davenport writes again, in 1663 :— "They have been blowing at the iron-works, and have run from the last sixth day to this second day five sows (beds?) of iron, which are commended for very good * * * and begin to-morrow to make pots." Captain Clark petitioned, in 1622, that wine and liquors might be used, customs free, at these works. Only one butt of wine and one barrel of liquor was allowed; but the clerk of the works afterwards received privilege to furnish liquor. In 1669 an exemption from taxes was granted Captain Clark for seven years, to encourage him in supplying the country with "good iron and well wrought according to art."

The early iron-works lay along the coast, and more than three-quarters of a century passed before the rich deposits, now known in Western Connecticut, were exploited. Oldmixon mentions, in 1741, a small iron-mill at New Brainford, now Brandford, near the Sound, on a stream (Stony creek). It may have been the mill for which Ebenezer Fitch & Co. received, in 1716, the exclusive right to erect slitting-mills in Connecticut during fifteen years. At Salisbury, then Weatog, the colony granted a tract of one hundred acres to Yale

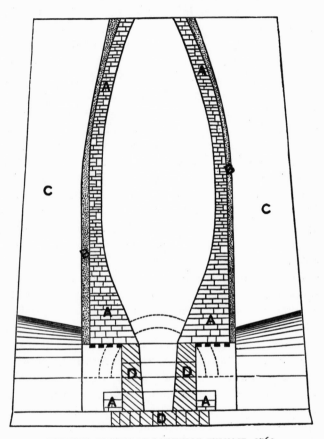

VERTICAL SECTION OF LAKEVILLE FURNACE, 1763.

EXPLANATION.

A. Slate used or in-walls (lining).
B. Yellow clay.
C. White limestone from the Lakeville quarries.
D. Refractory stone from Haverstraw, on the Hudson river.
Greatest diameter of interior of furnace, nine feet ; height, about twenty-eight feet.

College. Here ore was discovered in 1732, and the tract was transferred, in 1734, to Philip Livingston, of Albany, who built a furnace at Limerock, five miles from his ore-beds, and made castings in 1736. The rich Salisbury brown hematites proved such good ores that in 1762 John Hazeltine, Samuel Forbes, and Ethan Allen (of Ticonderoga fame) built another—the Lakeville furnace—at the outlet of Wanscopommuc lake, two miles east of the Ore-hill banks.

The Lakeville furnace was sold a year afterwards to Richard Smith, an Englishman, of Hartford, by whom it was rebuilt in 1770. Being a royalist, he left the country on the outbreak of the Revolution, and the State took possession of, but did not confiscate, the furnace; the Council of Safety spent £1450 on it to prepare it for casting cannon, shot, and shell for the colonial army.

Gouverneur Morris and John Jay superintended the proof of these guns, which stood the most severe tests creditably, none of them having been known to fail. The New York forts and the navy were armed with Salisbury cannon, the batteries of the Constellation and Constitution (Old Ironsides) frigates consisting entirely of them. Many of these guns were again used in the war of 1812. Beside cannon, &c., large potash-kettles, weighing nearly half a ton, were cast at the Lakeville furnace. It continued to be the only one in the region till 1810; it was occupied in 1831 by Messrs. Holley and Coffin, who made five hundred to six hundred tons of pig iron yearly. Many of those since built, and the Lakeville furnace itself, have been long since abandoned, and the group of Salisbury furnaces now in operation makes high-grade car-wheel iron almost exclusively. The section of the Lakeville furnace exhibits the shape of the old furnace, and, as it happens, that of others now in operation in the region. The first furnaces used an average of two hundred and fifty to three hundred bushels of charcoal and two and one-half to three tons of ore per ton of iron, and made three to three and one-half tons of iron daily. The pressure of the blast produced by the old bellows is not known, but the blast is now used at half to three-quarters of a pound per square inch. These old furnaces made eighteen to twenty tons a week, and ran four or five months yearly. The ore was at first mined without royalty, but after the Revolution twenty-five cents was fixed, which was raised by successive steps to one dollar and twenty-five cents in 1831. The Salisbury ore now averages in the furnace about two and one-third tons to the ton of iron; requires in the charcoal furnace in which it is worked about fourteen per cent. of limestone and one hundred to one hundred and fifty bushels of charcoal. The daily product of the present furnaces is ten to twelve tons of iron, and the duration of a single blast is often over two years.

At Minehill, in Roxbury township, Litchfield county, there exists a series of veins of spathic iron-ore, one of which is six feet across. These were known in 1750, and worked for silver by Hurlbut and Hawley, and the Bronson Brothers (1764), naturally in vain. A furnace built by a Mr. Bacon did not succeed in making iron of it with profit; but D. J. Styles made good steel from the iron. The mine was abandoned until the American Silver-Steel Company opened it again in 1865; this company erected an elliptical furnace, thirty-two feet high and ten and one-half by eight and one-half feet across the boshes, which was blown by a *McKenzie rotary blower*, and also forges and a small train for the manufacture of *German forge steel.* The effort was unsuccessful. The colony granted, in 1761, a loan of £1200 to Ephraim and John Patterson and Thomas Russell, to erect a furnace on the Housatonic river, in Kent,—probably near the great Kent mine. The present Kent furnace was, however, built originally in 1825.

In 1760 Messrs. Keny, Hull, Wooster, of Derby, and Perkins, of Enfield, obtained authority to purchase of the Indians a water-power for iron-works, near the falls of the Naugatuck.

The region around Kent, Saulsbury, and Amenia, now in New York, of which Limerock is now the central point, had several furnaces and many forges, supported by the high quality and extent of the ore deposits. The quality of the cold-blast charcoal iron was famed for guns, and of the forge iron for muskets. At Falls Village and Limerock two finery forges, with ten fires, made iron for the Government, but were abandoned, owing to its preference for Swedish iron. The Government was cheated by a false sample, and could get no more iron of equal quality; but the forges had been ruined, and did not resume. At the end of the eighteenth century the town of Milford had seven bloomeries; making three hundred tons of bar iron a year, and the county of Litchfield contained in all fifty bloomeries and three slitting-mills. None of these exist now.

The first *steel* made in America was probably made in Connecticut, since the colony in 1655 granted privileges to John Tucker of Southold, Long Island, in consideration of his making steel, but there is no record of his doings. In 1727 Joseph Higby memorialized the Legislature of Connecticut that he had " with great pains and cost to himself found out and obtained a curious art, by which to convert, change, or transmit common iron into good steel, sufficient for any use; and was the very first that ever performed such an operation in America." He produced samples of good steel, and obtained, with Joseph Dewey, a patent for ten years. This Joseph Higby was a blacksmith, of Granby, who, in 1737 and afterwards, struck up coins of copper from the Simsbury mines near by, known as the "Granby coppers," in the currency of the colony. For the dies he probably used his own steel.

It is noticeable that in 1761 (Phil. Trans. Royal Soc., 1763, vol. 53, page 48) iron was made from "black sand" (*i. e.*, magnetic-iron sand), in Connecticut, by George Eliot, a son of the distinguished Jared Eliot, who also had a steel furnace "erected several years before the act of Parliament prohibited them in the plantations." This iron was made in a common bloomery fire; the sand yielded sixty per cent., though it was reduced with some difficulty with the aid of fluxes (cinder from other iron and bog ore). It was in fine grains, and was washed clean from sand. Each heat produced apparently fifty pounds of iron from eighty-three pounds of sand-ore. The ore was as "capable of being wrought as rock-ore or bog mine," but it took "longer to smelt" than other ores, the time required being five hours, though it was afterwards reduced to three hours, and it was hoped to increase the weight of iron made to seventy pounds. This iron was made, apparently, in considerable quantities, and after conversion into steel (by G. Eliot) was tried in London by Horne, with the result that "the steel worked well and free from flaws." Eliot's *iron*, however, crumbled under the hammer, but was welded and worked "in a manner sound." The test "showed it to possess all the agreeable toughness and ductility for which the Spanish iron is so deservedly famous, without the vile redshire quality for which the latter is very remarkable." The letter of Jared Eliot, giving these descriptions of operations in his son's works, was dated Kenilworth, on the Sound, twenty-five miles east of New Haven, where the works probably were. Jared Eliot received the gold medal of the London Society of Arts for the discovery worked out by his son. G. Eliot is referred to, in 1785, by Rev. Daniel Little, of Boston,—who invented a process for cementation (in a mixture of two parts of dried seaweed and one part wood-ashes, mixed with water or urine to a thick paste), and employed Eliot to work it up,—as "Colonel Eliot, of Connecticut, a gentleman of ability in the steel way for many years." Mr. Little states that though steel had been made for many years in the United States, yet, so far as he knew, it was of inferior quality and little used for edge-tools.

NEW YORK.

The details of the early manufacture in New York are very scanty. The Dutch settlers under the Holland West India Company were aware of the existence of iron-ore, but Director-General Kieft was more intent on gold than iron, and the Patroons excepted all mineral rights from their deeds. Heinrich Van der Capellan reported the discovery of iron-ore in 1644, and in 1646 the company granted the discoverer of a mine the free right to its use for ten years, and after that one-tenth its proceeds as royalty.

The country, as far as Minisink, on the Delaware, was explored,—the minerals extracted being removed on a

well-constructed road leading thence to Esopus, on the
Hudson. But no iron appears to have been made by
the Dutch, possibly owing to the hatred their arbitrary
rule had excited among the Indians.) Hubbard wrote,
about 1680, that "Staten Island produces tin and store
of iron;" and Messrs Brooke and Nicol reported to the
Lords of Trade, in 1696, that there were some iron-
mines in the province, "but the iron is brittle and little
of it made." In 1720, in answer to the interrogatory
of the Lords, "What mines are there?" Brigadier Hunter said, "Iron enough;" and though Governor Colden,
in 1723, lauded the position of the ore, near deep water
in the "River," the dense woods, and the ample water-
power, yet Governor Cosby wrote, in 1734, that there
were then no iron-works in the province. Lieutenant-
Governor Clarke wrote to the Lords of Trade, in 1737,
that he had invited the attention of the Assembly to the
manufacture as one of lasting service; adding, in 1738,
that iron-works required more money "to bring them
to perfection" than lay at the command of the private
persons who owned the mines. This proposal of
Clarke's contemplated establishing, under the sanction
of the Assembly, a company for making bar iron and
raising hemp, the organization of which was to be
similar to that afterward established by Hasenclever.

The Ancram Iron-works, in Columbia county, on Jan-
sen's or Ancram creek, were built by Philip Livingston,
some time after 1734, and used ore from Salisbury,
Connecticut, and from mines in the eastern part of the
township. This works consisted of a blast-furnace and a
forge, and lay in the Livingston manor, Ancram being
the name of the native place of the family in Scotland.
In 1757 Governor DeLancey reported to the Lords of
Trade that the Ancram Iron-works had, in seven years,

between 1750 and 1756, inclusive, made three thousand three hundred and eighteen tons twelve hundred weight and one hundred pounds of pig iron, one thousand three hundred tons eight hundred weight of which had been converted into bar iron, and sixty-six tons fifteen hundred weight and twenty-one pounds into castings. He also reported no other works then in operation in the province.

IRON MADE AT ANCRAM.

YEAR.	PIG IRON.				MADE INTO BARS.		CASTINGS.			
	Tons.	Cwt.	Qrs.	Lbs.	Tons.	Cwt.	Tons.	Cwt.	Qrs.	Lbs.
1750................	43	3	3	13	195	15	5	2	3	7
1751................	606	6	3	17	164	12	6	1	2	0
1752......	354	7	3	0	183	14	3	2	1	14
1753................	22	9	2	0	215	16	2	3	0	21
1754................	0	0	0	0	211	5	4	2	2	0
1755................	722	2	3	0	149	16	36	2	3	7
1756................	267	14	0	14	182	0	10	0	0	0
	2016	4	3	16	1302	8	66	15	0	21
	1302	8	0	0	Per DIRCK JANSEN,					
Total............	3318	12	3	16	Storekeeper.					

De Lancey reported the above as an account of the *iron made in the province*, saying the Ancram was the only works carried on during those years. He continued:—"Several works have been begun, but were dropt through the mismanagement or inability of the undertakers. Of these there were two furnaces in the manor of Cortland and several bloomeries; but they have not been worked for several years past." The Ancram Works lay for some years under a novel disadvantage. The province of Massachusetts claimed jurisdiction westward to the Pacific Ocean, and sought to unsettle Livingston's titles to parts of the manor. In May, 1755, Mr. Livingston swore that all his employees were in the Springfield jail, and he could not furnish shot and carriage-wheels for the expeditions against Niagara and Crown Point, though he had prepared for the work at an expense of £400. The Ancram furnace was still in operation in 1837, but was soon after abandoned.

In 1750 Governor Clinton reported a plating-forge, with a tilt-hammer, in existence, but not in operation, at Wawayanda, in Orange county. This works lay twenty-six miles from the Hudson, and belonged to Lawrence Scrawley, a blacksmith of the county.) It was the only one in the province, and there were no slitting-mills or steel-furnaces. The Stirling Iron-works, in Orange county, were built in 1751, after the discovery of rich mines in 1750, and produced annually about one thousand five hundred tons of pig, which was worked into bar iron. They lay in Warwick township, close to the line of Monroe. They were built—a furnace and forge—by Ward & Colton as an anchor forge. The name originated in that of William Alexander (Lord Stirling), afterward a general of the continental army, who owned the land and was interested in the works. Before the Revolution this works passed into the hands of Peter Townsend, who, in 1776, made steel by the German process in the forge fire. The great iron chain drawn across the Hudson during the Revolution, each link of which weighed one hundred and forty pounds, the whole weighing one hundred and eighty-six tons, was forged at these works in six weeks, under the oversight of Colonel Timothy Pickering.

Near Ward & Colton's furnace Abel Nobel, from Pennsylvania, built a forge and made, in 1753, the first anchor produced in the vicinity. In 1772 Townsend built a second furnace on the property, near the outlet of Stirling pond. This furnace, five feet in the boshes by twenty-five feet high, has been in ruins for more than sixty years. The Long mine, belonging to Townsend, was the only one, except those opened by Hasenclever, in which systematic mining was at that time attempted; it was worked to a depth of one hundred and seventy feet, on a six-foot vein. These works remained in the Townsend family till about 1864.

Many mines were discovered in Orange county before the Revolution. The ore of one of these, the Mountain mine, half a mile south-west of the Long mine, produced iron so strong and so susceptible of a high polish that most of it was sent to England. There were many bloomeries built to work these ores, of which no record remains, and furnaces also abandoned for various reasons, after a short life. For instance, the Craigsville furnace, in operation during the Revolution, and the Haverstraw furnace, on the west side of the Tappan Zee, rebuilt in the present century, but never blown in.

In 1756 a furnace worked ore from the Forest of Dean mine, in a thick vein, six miles north-west-by-west of Fort Montgomery. Samuel Patrick cast stoves here in 1776 for the Government; but the furnace was abandoned in 1777.

In 1767, after he had built his four furnaces in New Jersey, Hasenclever began to build the fifth, in the Highlands, on the North river, forty miles above New York.

The site was chosen on account of the discovery of six mines. But the best veins thinned out and disappeared, while the ore from the others proved so inferior in every respect—"sulphurous, copperish, cold-shear, full of mundic and arsenical matter"—that the whole enterprise was abandoned. The expensive road, reservoir, log-houses, and furnace went for naught. The same misfortune overtook the Cortland furnace, also under Hasenclever's control.

A furnace and foundry were in operation in Amenia, Dutchess county, a mile from Wassaic station, during the Revolution. In Putnam county Peter Townsend had a mine at Simewog hill, in South-east, of rich magnetic ore, which was carted to Danbury, Connecticut, and also shipped by water to various furnaces. In fact, the whole of the Highlands along the Hudson were known to contain iron-ore; but the explorations had in many instances resulted unfortunately. Even if the mines produced the finest ore, the distance from market was often an insuperable obstacle; and a road was then as important to an iron-works as a hammer to the forge. In 1783 the cost of carriage of one ton of merchandise from New York City to the Canadian boundary, on Lake Champlain, was estimated by William Gilliland at eleven pounds sterling; the land-carriage from Albany to Fort George, a distance of sixty-five miles, alone amounted to six pounds eight shillings, at two shillings per mile. Hence, proximity to a market or water carriage was necessary to the existence of any of the early works.

In 1765 William Gilliland, a rich merchant of New York, gave up trade with the purpose of founding, on the shore of Lake Champlain, a vast estate, which he could lease, like a British noblemen, to his tenants. The region came into undisputed British possession in 1763, by the treaty of Paris with the French, and in 1768 Gilliland located large tracts along the shore between Crown Point and the Boquet river, having previously induced many Irish settlers to proceed thither. Although travelers had previously noticed the presence of iron sand on the lake and on the banks of the streams, Gilliland did not pay special attention to it, though he visited the Trois Rivieres forge, near Montreal, with interest, describing it as in very bad condition. His energies were directed to farming and the lumber trade. After the Revolution, in which, though a patriot, he was ruined, mainly by the baseness of Benedict Arnold, he prepared to raise ore and erect iron-works, and to his sagacity is due the initiation of the iron industry. He received an offer July 31st, 1780, from "Joseph Carder, of Scituate, Rhode Island, fourteen miles from Providence, of sixpence, lawful money, per ton for iron-ore," Carder agreeing to raise it at his own expense and mine five hundred to one thousand tons annually. In March, 1783, John Gilbert, the "owner of Berkshire furnace, in Lenox," also proposed to raise ore on royalty, as shown by Gilliland's Journal. He did not complete his plans, however, for he perished in a winter storm in 1796, while returning home alone after surveying a tract of land.

The Trois Rivieres Works, for many years the only one in Canada, and which supplied guns, shot, kettles, utensils, edge-tools, bar iron, &c. to the French, was visited by Kalm in 1749. It lay three miles west of the village of the same name, and about midway between Quebec and Montreal, which, with Trois Rivieres, were then the three principal towns of Canada. Kalm says:—
" Here are two great forges, besides two lesser ones to each of the great ones, and under the same roof with them. The bellows were made of wood and everything else, as it is in *Swedish* forges. The melting-ovens stand close to the forges, and are the same as ours. The ore is got two *French* miles and a half from the

iron-works, and is carried thither on sledges. It is a
kind of moor ore (*Tophus Tubalcaini, Linn. Syst. Nat.*
III., page 187, n. 5), which lies in veins, within six
inches or a foot from the surface of the ground. Each
vein is six to eighteen inches deep, and below it is a
white sand. The veins are surrounded with this sand
on both sides, and covered at the top with a thin mould.
The ore is pretty rich, and lies in loose lumps in the
veins, of the size of two fists, though there are a few
which are near eighteen inches thick. These lumps
are full of holes, which are filled with ochre. The ore
is so soft that it may be crushed between the fingers.
They make use of a gray limestone for promoting the
fusibility of the ore; for this purpose they also employ
a clay marl, which is found near this place. Charcoal
is to be had in great abundance here, because all the
country round this place is covered with woods, which
have never been stirred. The charcoal from evergreen
trees, that is from the fir kind, is best for the forge;
but those of deciduous trees are best for the smelting-
oven. The iron which is here made was described to
me as soft, pliable, and tough, and is said to have the
quality of not being attacked by rust so easily as other
iron; and in this point there appears a great difference
between the *Spanish* iron and this in shipbuilding."
This works was built in 1737, by individuals, and soon
afterwards sold to the king of France. Attempts to
make steel succeeded partially, but were not followed,
for want of knowledge. The iron-works did not pay
expenses, which was attributed by the overseers to the
sparse population and high wages; but the ore was easy
to work, the iron good, and the business was a monopoly. The officers and men, however, were observed
to be in affluent circumstances.

We find that the first iron-works of any kind—a bloomery—in the region, was built at Willsboro Falls, on the Boquet, in 1801, using the dam of one of Gilliland's old saw-mills. Levi Highby, George Throop, and Charles Kane, of Schenectady, built it to make "anchors and mill forgings," under a ten-year contract with parties in Troy. This was, for many years, the only works in the region, and it is rather surprising to find that for the first ten years it used ore from Basin Harbor, in Vermont, and some from Canada. It is stated that the bed at Basin Harbor was the only ore then known in the country. It is certain that the discovery and working of the present ore-beds of the region dates only to the beginning of the present century.

Lord Sheffield stated that the exports from the port of New York, for the year ending July 5th, 1766, were five hundred and thirty-two tons of bar iron, worth twenty-six pounds sterling per ton, and five hundred tons pig iron, worth seven pounds ten shillings sterling per ton. In 1775 the shipments amounted to two thousand four hundred tons of pig iron and seven hundred and fifty tons of bar iron; and in 1776 they were eight hundred tons of pig iron and six hundred and ninety tons of bar iron. The pig iron was then valued at three pounds fifteen shillings sterling, and the bar iron at seventeen pounds sterling per ton.

NEW JERSEY.

The New Jersey iron-works were thus described in 1685, by Budd ("Good Order in Pennsylvania and New Jersey"), "One iron-works already in East Jersey." These were Colonel Lewis Morris' works at Tinton Falls, Monmouth county, and were doubtless the first in the colony. Tinton Falls was probably originally Tintern Falls, named after the Tintern Abbey Works, in Monmouthshire, England. The Tintern Abbey furnace was the *first charcoal-furnace which used a blast compressed in cast-iron cylinders*, getting thereby double the iron the bellows used to melt. The grant of ore-right was made to Morris in 1676; it embraced over three thousand five hundred acres in the triangle south-east of the Raritan, but probably the present Shrewsbury river is meant, and between it, the Whale Pond (a stream), and the sea, and stipulated payment of damages only from roads or trespass of cattle to the owners of the land. Colonel Morris was an English merchant, from Barbados, and O'Callaghan believes that he bought these works of John Grover, who, in 1655, rebelled here against the dominion of the Dutch; the province passed out of their hands to the English in 1664, and was settled by New England emigrants. In 1682 the East Jersey proprietaries state that a furnace and forge were already set up, which made good iron. Morris employed sixty to seventy negroes. In December, 1741, Morris addressed a memorial to the Lords of Trade, praying for encouragement of the manufacture of iron in New Jersey.

The bog ores of the sluggish streams on the eastern sea-coast furnished material for the early iron-works, being more easily won than the magnetic ores of the interior; and, spite of the superior quality of the latter, iron-making from bog ore did not cease till recently. The early works in Eastern Massachusetts depended largely on this region, and so did the earliest Pennsylvania works. The mines at Egg Harbor, which supplied the Plymouth furnaces with ore, were worked till 1830, and supplied, at one time, about thirty bloomeries. But nearly all the bloomeries were abandoned before 1830, and the district is now unproductive. It is an interesting fact that Rogers' description (New Jersey Reports, 1840, page 296) of the formation of this bog ore corresponds almost exactly with that given by Dr. Thatcher of the formation of the Plymouth ore.

On the tributaries of the Little Egg Harbor river lie two great deposits—the principal ones—of bog or swamp ore. The westernmost of these extends from the Atsion river in a belt, about three miles wide, to Landing creek, about twenty miles. The eastern deposit lies along the waters of Tulpehaukin or Wading river, but is inferior in extent to the former. The ore is derived from the ferruginous percolations from the green sand into undrained soils, and was classed as *loam ore, seed ore*, and *massive ore*. The percentage of iron varied from forty to fifty-three per cent. The three kinds were generally found in one hole, in the order given,—the loam ore nearest the surface.

In 1766 Charles Reed built the Batsto furnace, on Little Egg Harbor river, below Atsion, which ran till about 1855. It was mentioned in the Journals of the Continental Congress as "Dr. Coxe's iron-works, in the Jerseys," and cast shot for the army. Before the Revolution many works, principally bloomeries, were built in this region, and in 1769 the Assembly of the province granted the owners of iron-works in the townships of Evesham and Northampton special privileges. In New Jersey, and especially in this part of it, the abundant ore was utilized in clearing the forests, so that instead of being burnt as they lay, the trees were coaled and contributed, through the bloomeries, to the prosperity of the State.

The rich and pure magnetic ores of Northern New

Jersey, in the region now included in Morris, Passaic,
Warren, and Sussex counties, were known to the Dutch at
an early date, but not worked on account of the troubles
with the Swedes, as described hereafter, under the head
of Pennsylvania. The earliest mine opened on magnetic
ore was the Suckasunny mine, in the town of Randolph,
the mass of which was pure magnetic ore, practically
free from gangue. It was known to the Indians, who
named the locality by the words denoting in their
tongue "*black stone*," now corrupted to Suckasunny.
The mine was opened in 1710, the ore being at first
free; but the land was bought by Joseph Kirkbride,
in 1707, from the East Jersey proprietors. Owing to
British restrictions little was done by Kirkbride's
family. It passed from their hands into those of Dickerson and Minard La Fevre. Little enterprise was
exhibited till 1807, when it became the property of
Mahlon Dickerson, in whose family it still remains.
It supplied many bloomeries in the region. The
townships of Randolph and Rockaway include some
of the richest mines in the State, and formed the principal district of operations with magnetic ore before
the Revolution. Near these mines there were, in
Hanover township, many bloomeries,—one at Imlaystown, built in 1716, and another at Whippany, built in
the same year. The owner of the Imlaystown bloomery,
alluding to the decline of the trade under British restrictions, used to say that at first the state of his business
was "go penny, come pound, but he had carried it on
till it became go pound, come penny." The Whippany
forge, said to be the first bloomery in Morris county,
lay on the Whippany, near Morristown, close to the
present track of the Morris and Essex Railroad. Its
ore was brought in leathern bags eight or ten miles

H. C. DEL.

W. ORR N.Y.

DICKERSON MINE IN 1855.

from Dickerson's mine. The bar iron was packed to
market in the same way. The bars were cut so as
to be easily carried, and a horse would make about
fifteen miles a day, under a load of four to five hundred pounds. The Petersburg bloomery, in Morris
county, was built in 1725. It was rebuilt in 1850, but
abandoned after the Rebellion. The Troy forge, in Hanover, was built in 1745, and was still running in 1859,
making forty tons of bar iron yearly, but is now also
abandoned.

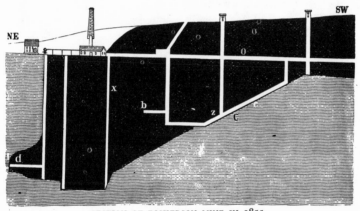

SECTION OF DICKERSON MINE IN 1855.

The quality of the New Jersey bar iron in 1737 is
described by Henry Calvert in two letters to John
Bannister, the agent of Messrs Crowley & Co. He
writes from New York, under date of June 7th, "there
are sundry forges in the Jerseys where they draw bar
iron tolerably well. I have seen it broke, and it appears
most white with a small mixture of black-tough. The
smiths give about twenty-four shillings per hundred-
weight for it, this money. *They slit all their bar iron by
hand.* The person who has the ship-works says he has

twenty-one shillings per hundred-weight for his work (thimbles and small work included), and the owners find the bar iron." Again, on July 2d, he writes, "this day I have seen a piece of bar iron from the Jerseys, which is pretty well drawn; got the smith to break three bars cold. They are all white-tough, without any mixture of black red-short." He probably saw bars made from the bog ores of East Jersey. White-tough he uses to denote cold-short iron; his discrimination between the characteristic colors of red and cold-short iron shows he understood the subject.

The Oxford furnace, in Warren county, was built between 1745 and 1755, but its mines were opened in 1743. Its iron used to be carried in Durham boats down the Delaware, from Foul Rift, to Philadelphia. It was, probably, excepting Cornwall, the *only one of the earliest furnaces* which remained in 1859, but has been altered from its original dimensions, eight foot bosh and thirty-eight feet high, to an anthracite furnace. The Hibernia furnace was built before 1764, in Pequannock township, Morris county, seven miles from Charlottenburg, and was employed by Congress during the Revolution. This furnace must have been built and owned by William Alexander, Lord Stirling, as he leased it in 1772 to John Jacob Faesch. Its manager, Joseph Huff, wrote, November 21st, 1776, that it was the only furnace in the province which he knew to be then in blast. He desired salt to barter for provisions, that he might not stop during the winter. Hasen-clever said that in 1764 this furnace made seventeen tons per week out of the same ore from which his Charlottenburg furnace made twenty-eight tons, and ascribes the difference to "a good furnace and an experienced, able founder." Beech Glen bloomery, in the same township, was built in 1760, and was abandoned after the Civil War, with more than a hundred years of service.

Three miles north-west of Rockaway lie the Mount Hope mines, a most important series of deposits—nine in all. When discovered, the "Great Jugular" vein jutted out of the ground, like a cliff, at a point a few rods west of the old Mount Hope House. Colonel Jacob Ford, of Morristown, bought a section of land (six thousand four hundred acres) here in 1770, and built in that year the stone-house above mentioned. On one of its window-panes there was long visible (1853) the inscription, "Samuel Ogden, 1778," written with a diamond.

In 1772 John Jacob Faesch, a German, bought the Ford property, as well as an adjoining section, and built the Mount Hope furnace, in 1772. He soon leased the Hibernia furnace from Lord Stirling. He made hollow ware, cannon-balls, &c., and probably exported pig iron to England. During the Revolution these two furnaces furnished a vast number of cannon-balls to the Continental army. It is said that after the battle of Trenton, in 1776, Faesch employed thirty Hessian prisoners, being merely at the expense of guarding and feeding them. After the close of the Revolution, "hundreds of tons of balls" remained in store at these furnaces, and were finally removed by Government to Governor's Island. These furnaces were torn down nearly half a century ago.

Faesch's estate was broken up very early in the present century; it included many valuable mines, since discovered, among others the Swedes mine. This mine was discovered by John Howard, a miner at Hibernia, in Stephen Jackson's employ. Howard was taking a short cut home from Rockaway, through the woods, and noted an enormous deviation of his compass at a point where he was resting. After the death of Faesch this mine and much of his property came into the hands of Stephen and Colonel Joseph Jackson, at that time the most active miners and iron-makers in Morris county.

In Hunterdon county the Union furnace got its ore from Clinton, where mines were opened early in the eighteenth century, the furnace itself being abandoned in 1778. Acrelius (1759) mentions the Union Iron-works, belonging, with twelve thousand acres of land, to William Allen and Thomas Turner. They had two mines. The one most used was twenty feet deep, the ore at the surface being contaminated with sulphur and copper; but under the surface ore good for all purposes was found in plenty. There were two furnaces and two forges, each with two stacks; also, a trip-hammer and a flatting hammer. Judge Allen stated that the ores at his works and at Durham, Pennsylvania, yielded a ton of pig iron to one and a half tons of ore, the furnaces averaging twenty to twenty-five tons per week when in blast. A forge with three fires made two tons per week, and a clear profit of six pounds twelve shillings and eight pence sterling. It cost two pounds eight shillings (New Jersey currency) to convert pig into bar iron, and the pig iron "should not cost over two pounds sterling per ton," while bar iron costs ten pounds sterling at the forge.

In Franklin village, eighteen miles north of Dover, Morris county, the Franklin furnace was built in 1770, but all trace of the original furnace has long since disappeared. The character of its ore rendered it famous (viz., Franklinite, composed of iron manganese and zinc oxides), but all attempts to work the ore direct were fruitless. The ore is now, however, smelted after the extraction of its zinc, and produces *spiegeleisen* (pig iron, with not less than eight per cent. of manganese nor four per cent. of carbon) fit for use in the manufacture of Bessemer steel. Mr. Edwin Post succeeded in working this ore by itself in a Catalan forge, and made excellent bar iron, the strength of which exceeded that of any kind ever tested at the *Forges Nationales de la Chassande*. Its absolute tenacity was forty and eight-tenths kilogrammes per millimetre, or fifty-seven thousand four hundred and nineteen pounds per square inch; and no iron tested there, either English, Swedish, Spanish, or Siberian, had reached forty kilogrammes. Bornet, the director of the works, reported July 12th, 1850, that the iron was entirely *fibrous*, worked finely, and could be perfectly welded. The strength, however, corresponds much better with the hard iron the ore would be likely to make than with the soft iron reported.

The Journals of the Continental Congress thus allude to the Andover Iron-works, in Sussex county, forty miles from New York, which were in operation before the Revolution. Resolution passed January 15th, 1778:—"The Board of War shall contract, through Colonel Flower, with Whithead Humphreys, for steel for continental artificers and works; and, as the iron made at the Andover works only will, with certainty, answer the purpose, Colonel Flower be directed to apply to the governor of New Jersey to put a person in to put these works in blast (they belong to persons who adhere to the enemies of the States)." Mr. Humphreys was a steelmaker of Philadelphia, as we shall see. The steel was of a superior quality, reported equal to that made from Swedish or Russian iron. The mines lay idle till 1847, when they were opened by Cooper, Hewitt & Co., and proved equal to their old reputation.

The most important group of iron-works in the colony before the Revolution was that built in Morris and Passaic (formerly Bergen) counties, by Peter Hasenclever, a German, born at Remscheid, in 1716. Having left Cadiz, where he was a merchant, he went to London, in 1763, organized the firm of Hasenclever, Seton & Crofts, and in 1764 induced the American or London Company, as it is sometimes called, consisting of General Graeme, Commodore Forrest, Secretary Jackson, of the admiralty, and others, to agree to spend from £10,000 to £40,000 in the manufacture of pig iron, pot and pearl ashes, and the production of hemp. Hasenclever represented the American Company in America; and he, or his firm rather, acted as brokers in handling and selling its products. He arrived at New York in June, with hundreds of German workmen, and in August, 1765, shipped bar iron, as well as five hogsheads of potash, to London.

Within three years he built the following works:— At Charlottenburg, on the west branch of the Pequanock river, in 1767, a blast-furnace, capable of making twenty to twenty-five tons of iron per week; three miles lower down the stream he built a finery forge, with four fires and two hammers, "capable of making two hundred and fifty tons of bar iron a year single-handed, and from three hundred to three hundred and fifty tons double-handed." About a mile lower down he built a second forge of equal capacity. About thirteen miles from Charlottenburg, on a more northerly branch of the Pequanock, called Ringwood river, he purchased the property of an abandoned iron-works. The location of this works was a short distance below the present village of Stirling Works. Here he erected a new blast-furnace, like that at Charlottenburg, and within fifty yards of the furnace a forge, with three fires and two hammers, and "a *stamping-mill for separating the iron from the cinder*, in the old cinder-bank." About five hundred yards above the furnace he built another forge, with four fires and two hammers; half a mile below the furnace a third forge, with two fires and one hammer; and two miles lower down stream he placed a fourth forge, of the same size as the last,—in all eleven fires. He bought the Ringwood property for its ore; but the old mines failed, or became inferior in quality, and the location proved fortunate only through the discovery of the Good Hope mine, in 1767, on Wales mountain, about a mile and a half west of the furnace. This vein was proved for about a mile, and showed in some places a width of fourteen feet.

Three and a half miles south-west of Ringwood, Hasenclever built a third series of works on a stream (Winockie) issuing from Longpond and falling into Ringwood river, about four miles below the furnace. This Longpond is the present Greenwood pond, and these works are the *recent* Ringwood works, the old ones being located as above. The works lay two miles from the outlet of the pond, and consisted of a furnace like the previous ones, in blast in 1768, and a forge, with four fires and two hammers. Each of these works had all necessary shops, buildings, dwellings, and a saw-mill, and the Charlottenburg works two saw-mills; while at Ringwood there was a good grist-mill. Expensive, long roads were built for communication in all necessary directions. The works were often stopped by drought in summer, and to remedy this vast reservoirs were provided for water storage. For Charlottenburg the Makopin and Dunken ponds were utilized and raised by a dam several feet above their natural surface. Near Ringwood the Toxito (now Truxedo) pond was cut off from the Ramapo, its natural drainage line, by a dam eight hundred and sixty feet long and from twelve to twenty-two feet high, and joined by a canal to the Ringwood river. At Longpond a dam, two hundred feet in length, raised the water about four feet, providing an ample reserve.

Beside the furnaces above mentioned, Hasenclever built one probably near Pompton, and on the lower part of Ringwood river; one at Haverstraw, New York, and one at Cortland, in Westchester county, New York; but was obliged to abandon them because the veins of ore thinned out or "turned out sulphurous, copperish, cold-shear, full of mundic and arsenical matters."

Hasenclever's operations were vast. His acquisitions of land covered fifty thousand acres in New Jersey and in Orange county, New York, a patent of eighteen thousand acres in Herkimer county, and six thousand seven hundred and fifty-five acres near German flats, besides forty thousand acres in Nova Scotia, and eleven thousand five hundred acres on Lake Champlain, north of Crown Point. In two years he had spent £54,600, and though his bar iron was acknowledged to be the "best drawn which had ever made its appearance on the London market from America," yet his potash was inferior and unremunerative, and his hemp failed to grow.)

With a view of making a more valuable article than bar iron, he made all his arrangements for making steel in his forge fires. When in London, in 1767, he engaged three German "steel-smiths" to come to

America; but the enterprise fell, "for before these men had left Germany the American Company (or rather, I may say, their trustees, for none of the other partners found fault with me) perfidiously suspended me from all transactions in the American Company's affairs." One of Hasenclever's workmen had made from the ore steel which was considered good in America, and on being tested in London was pronounced excellent. This kind of steel was known for a long time in New Jersey only as "Hasenclever's steel.")

He was bankrupted, in 1766, by the dishonesty of his partner, Seton, and the extravagance, or rather the large scale, of his own operations. He made an arrangement with his partners and returned to America in 1768, as their agent, but was formally declared bankrupt in 1770. He claimed that the managers of the iron-works sent over from England were incompetent, and that the American Company was conspiring against him. This company requested Governors Clinton and Franklin to take steps in the court of chancery to prevent Hasenclever from interfering with the works, and Governor Franklin, of New Jersey, also appointed a committee, at Hasenclever's own request, to examine into the matter.

This body, consisting of Lord Stirling, Colonel John Schuyler, Major Tuines Dey, and James Grey, testified to the perfection of his iron-works, the quality of his iron, and to the fact that he had introduced many improvements in the manufacture, some of which had been adopted in England. They said, "He is the first person that we know who has so greatly improved the use of the great natural ponds of this country, as by damming them to secure reservoirs of water for the use of iron-works in the dry season, without which the best streams are liable to fail in the great droughts we are subject to." They further said that Hasenclever was the first to make old cinder-beds profitable. One of his managers, Thomas Jordan, introduced the stamping-mill process into Staffordshire, England. He improved the furnace by building the in-walls "of slate" instead of "stones, which seldom lasted longer than a year or two," and by placing the stack under roof. He used only over-shot wheels, and "armed the hammer-wheel shafts with strong cast-iron rings, whose arms served as cogs to lift the hammer-handle." The commission, reporting at Newark, July 8th, 1768, specified these contrivances as new ones; "at least they are new in America." It was qualified to speak authoritatively, as its members were all interested in iron-works and mines.

In 1769 Hasenclever proceeded to London to free himself by a sale of his lands and an exposure of the frauds practiced on him. Many years afterwards (1790) he obtained redress, through a decision of Lord Thurlow. There is no doubt as to his ability, for he introduced the linen manufacture at Schmiedeberg, in Silesia, managing it with such success that, after the Revolution, he refused an advantageous invitation of Franklin to return to America.

Before his departure from America, Hasenclever was succeeded by Mr. Humfray, who was general manager at Charlottenberg, Ringwood, and Longpond when the commission reported. He was displaced by Philip Faesch, an incompetent man, who was, in his turn, shortly succeeded by Robert Erskine, F. R. S., who found the business of the company in great disorder, yet systematized its affairs so efficiently that there was some prospect of success. But the outbreak of the Revolution forced him to sell out the property, which he did, transmitting the proceeds to the owners while the war was in progress. Being the only educated civil engineer in America, he was appointed by Washington chief of staff and engineer corps, with the title of "Surveyor-general and Geographer-in-chief to the armies of the United States." He served in this capacity till his death in 1780, and was buried at Ringwood, where Washington erected a marble tomb over his remains.

In regard to the trade of his time, Hasenclever made some very interesting statements. He set out to build five blast-furnaces and seven forges, with twelve hammers and twenty-three fires. He estimated the cost of building these works at about £40,000, and the profits from them at £10,000 at least,—the furnaces producing three thousand five hundred tons pig iron yearly, at a profit of two pounds eleven shillings four pence sterling, and the forges one thousand two hundred and fifty tons bar iron yearly, at a profit of seven pounds thirteen shillings sterling per ton.

The actual costs of producing pig and bar iron are thus detailed:—

Effective Account of the Expenses and Wages paid in the Province of New Jersey, in North America, to smelt five tons of Ore into three tons of Pig Iron, and to reduce three tons of Pig Iron into two tons of Bar Iron.

To 5 tons of ore, with all charges rendered,
at the furnace, 15s. per ton,   .   .   . £3 15 0
9 loads of charcoal, of 96 bushels each, at 20s.
per load, ...   9   0 0

Carried forward, £12 15 0

Brought forward, £12 15 0

Wages—1 founder, at 5s. per day, and 9 as-
sistants, viz., 1 keeper, 2 fillers, 2 ore-
breakers, 2 coal-stockers, 1 gutterman,
and 1 bankman, at 3s. per day, . . . 1 12 0

Salaries and repair of buildings and roads per
day, ... 1 0 0

£15 7 0

Three tons of pig iron cost, at 180 per cent.,
£8 10s. 6d. sterling, which is £2 16s. 10d.
at the furnace, ... £2 16 10

Transport to New York, freight to London,
and charges in London, per ton, . . 3 0 5⅔

£5 17 3⅔

Profit, ... 1 2 8⅓

Pig iron sold in London, in 1764, at £7 0 0

Instead of three the Charlottenburg furnace made
four tons per day.

Expenses to reduce three tons of pig iron into two
tons of bar iron:—

To 3 tons of pig iron, ... £15 7 0

9 loads of coal, at 96 bushels per load, at
20s., ... 9 0 0

Forgemen's wages, at £4 5s. per ton, . . 8 10 0

Salaries and repair of buildings and roads,
at £3 per ton, ... 6 0 0

Carried forward, £38 17 0

Brought forward,	£38	17	0
Transport to New York and shipping, per ton, £1 10s., ...	3	0	0

Two tons of bar iron on board ship at New York cost, in New York currency, .	£41	17	0

Reduced at 180 per cent., this is £23 5s. sterling, or per ton, ...	£11	12	6
Freight to London, at £1 10s. per ton, .	1	10	0
Commission, insurance, and charges in London, ...	1	3	1

A ton of American bar iron delivered in London cost	£14	5	7
Profit per ton, ...	3	4	5

In 1764 bar iron sold in London at . .	£17	10	0

The forgemen who had agreed with Hasenclever to make bar iron at fourteen shillings four pence sterling per ton, got, during his absence, two pounds seven shillings two pence per ton, and he found he required two hundred and eighty-five bushels of charcoal per ton of pig iron, instead of one hundred and thirty-three bushels used in Germany. On the other hand, as some offset to the exorbitant wages, the ironmasters sold goods and provisions to their people, and estimated the profits thence arising at one pound ten shillings sterling per ton of bar iron.

In explanation of the poor quality of the charcoal, Hasenclever states that Colonel Ford, of Morristown, "one of the first adventurers in bloomery iron-works," ascribed it to its age, the Indians having injured the roots of the trees by firing the woods in hunting. A quarter to a third less charcoal was used when made from trees eighteen years old.

The expenses of making bar iron at Ringwood, out of the old material extracted from the cinder-heaps, is stated as follows, for four tons one hundred weight two quarters:—

To 3½ tons of cinder iron, at £1 10s., New York currency, per ton, . .	£5	5	0
5 tons old forge cinders, at £1 per ton, .	5	0	0
21¾ loads of charcoal, at 96 bushels per load, at 20s., ...	21	15	0
Forgemen's wages, at £5 14s. per ton (one-third more than for common bar), .	23	3	11
	£55	3	11

Reduced at 180 per cent., this is £30 13s. 4d. sterling for four tons one hundred weight and two quarters.

One ton cinder bar iron, at forge, . .	£7	10	7
Transport to New York, freight to London, and charges there, per ton, . . .	3	11	1½
One ton in London cost	£11	1	8½

This cinder iron was found particularly good for wagon-tires, ploughshares, &c. It was tough, and "almost as hard as steel."

About 1740 a committee of Parliament was informed by the governor that there were in New Jersey no manufactories of iron worth mentioning. In 1750 the governor reported to the Lords of Trade that there were one slitting-mill, not in use; one plating-forge, to work with a tilt-hammer, also not in use, and one steel-furnace.

Acrelius mentions the following works in operation in New Jersey in 1759:—The Union Iron-works, heretofore described, and four other furnaces at Oxford, Sterling, Ogden's, near Newton, Sussex county, and the Mount Holly furnace, each with its mines. In the latter bog ore was used, and its iron was fit for castings only.

The slitting-mill alluded to may have been the one at Split Rock, owned by David Ogden in 1770, which was believed to be the first built in the State. For the purpose of concealment the upper part of the building was a grist-mill, the lower half towards the river being the slitting-mill. The rolling-mill was worked by stealth, and when, in 1750, all the colonial works of this class were destroyed, Governor William Franklin and suite visited the Split Rock mill. But Samuel Ogden, the manager, whose father was then part owner, was noted for shrewdness and for his choice liquors. After a hospitable entertainment, neither the governor nor his suite could find any slitting-mill at all. Franklin himself was reputed a part owner of the works,—an additional reason for not seeing too much.

In 1774 Jacob Miller shipped bar iron from Dover to London, and in 1775 Thomas Mayberry made sheet iron at Mount Holly. Congress ordered of the latter, in May, 1775, five tons of sheet iron, for camp-kettles for the army. During the Revolution steel for the army was made at Trenton.

Iron manufacture suffered, especially in New Jersey, during the Revolution and for some years before it. At the outbreak of hostilities the Hibernia furnace was the only one actually in blast, though doubtless the Mount Hope was fully prepared. Erskine having closed and sold the Charlottenburg and Ringwood works, entered the army, and doubtless most of his neighbors followed his course,—those who sympathized with England being expelled the province.

After the Revolution, however, the iron industry of New Jersey gained a sure foothold about 1780, and fifteen or more forges were built in Morris and Passaic counties, between 1780 and 1790. Tench Coxe states that, by a return made in 1784, New Jersey had eight blast-furnaces and seventy-nine forges. An estimate, made about ten years after, placed the production of the State at one thousand two hundred tons of bar iron, eighty tons nail rods, and one thousand two hundred tons of pig iron yearly.

PENNSYLVANIA.

Iron-making in New Jersey and Pennsylvania was greatly retarded by the existence of a hearty hatred between the Dutch on the Hudson and the Swedes on the Delaware. In 1646 the Dutch attempted to prospect for iron-ore in Pennsylvania, at Minnesink and Durham, but were prevented from accomplishing anything by the Swedes, who excited the fears and jealousy of the Indians. The Swedes themselves were, on the death of Gustavus, practically abandoned by Christina, and fell into the hands of the Dutch, after a series of conflicts. The Dutch were in turn expelled by the English, under whom the iron manufacture sprang up as the fruit of individual enterprise. When Penn obtained the grant of Pennsylvania from Charles II. in 1681, and bought the domain of Delaware from the Duke of York, in 1682, he did nothing to encourage manufactures. In a letter written to the Society of Free

Traders, just after the purchase, Penn does not mention iron, though alluding to the resources of the colony. This society was composed of persons who purchased lands of Penn at ten cents an acre, with a view to settle the colony, doing so in person and by employees. As regards his territory, Penn pursued purely a speculative policy, very different from that adopted by Winthrop, Spottswood, and Gouge.

Iron-ore was, however, discovered and worked soon after Philadelphia was laid out. Richard Frame, who wrote a description of Pennsylvania in 1692, said, in his poetical text:—

> " If men would venture for to dig below,
>   They may get well by it, for aught I know :
>   Those Treasures in the Earth which hidden be,
>   They will be good, whoever lives to see.
>   A certain place here is, where some begun
>   To try some Mettle, and have made it run,
>   Wherein was Iron absolutely found,
>   At once was known about some Forty Pound."

In 1702, in answer to the desire of Penn to be informed as to the existence of a reported iron-mine, James Logan wrote that he had " spoken to the chief of those concerned in the iron-mines; but they seem careless, never having had a meeting. Their answer is they have not yet found any considerable vein."

The first mention of iron-making in Pennsylvania in the Minutes of Council, is February 24th, 1726, where it is stated that "several companies (are) already engaged in carrying on iron-works."

Emanuel Swedenborg, writing in 1734 (*Regnum Subteranneum sine Minerale de Ferro*), describes the early Pennsylvania works thus [translated from the original Latin]:—

"About nine years ago a furnace was built by the governor of the region, Sir William Keith, near the river Christina, which, during its first two years, produced quite a quantity of iron, but was abandoned in the third year for want of ore. They say the ore of that region is rich in iron, but too dry and without calcareous flux. At the distance of a mile thence another furnace was built, but made no iron. Now, however, ore is reduced there in hearths, like those used for refining pig iron. A similar works is situated near St. James' Church, on the Huitleer river, and belongs to Master John Ball [?John Hall], but has only one hearth. A larger works was built on the Schuylkill river by Master Samuel Nutt, with a furnace and hearths. Another, about six miles from this, belongs to Master M. Rutter. Further, near the river Delaware, are two works of this kind, whence pig iron is sent to England, as well as from the Principio furnace previously mentioned. There are at other places several works where the ore is smelted in common hearths, called *bloomeries*. At present five works are established near the Delaware river, and besides these four or more others are enumerated.

"The furnaces are twenty-five feet high, the opening into which ore and charcoal are charged being oblong and about four feet in length. The largest bellows are five feet wide. The ore is roasted, and oyster-shells are used as flux. Eighteen pecks of ore are charged to twenty-four bushels of charcoal. The furnace is tapped every eight hours, and about fifteen hundred weight got at a cast, or forty-five hundred weight per day.

"The refining of crude iron is done in forges and hearths. It is said that an English ton of wrought iron can be refined and forged out of pigs in twenty-four hours. The ton costs them thirty-five pounds sterling

in the currency of that region. One ton of pig iron
costs about nine pounds to ten pounds sterling.

"Direct reduction in forges and bloomery hearths.
Three pecks to one bushel of roasted ore are reduced
into a mass weighing sixty to seventy pounds, which
is, within four hours, forged out into rods or bars. The
hammer weighs three hundred pounds. The ore is
brought from places quite distant and inland."

The quality of this bar iron was good. Joseph Farmer,
a steel-maker of Birmingham, heretofore quoted (page
10), testified before a Committee of Parliament, in 1736,
that he had tried the Potomac iron, but found it too
tender, though fit for ordinary uses. Pennsylvania iron
he had tried in every form but steel, and found it entirely
fit for all purposes. William Donne, of Bristol, said to
the same committee that he had tried to convert Pennsylvania iron into steel, but it could not be altered,
though it was changed (in the converting-furnace) a
little from iron.

The first forge in Pennsylvania seems to have been
that of John Ball, above mentioned; the second that of
Nutt, the Coventry forge on French creek, Chester
county,—this was in operation in 1720. Rutter is,
however, mentioned as building the first forge, in the
following extract from the *Pennsylvania Gazette* of
March 13th, 1729:—"On Sunday last died here
Thomas Rutter, Senior. He was the first that erected
an iron-works in Pennsylvania." This statement is
supported by a letter of Jonathan Dickinson, in 1717,
stating that Rutter, "of his own strength, has set up
on making iron, and we have heard of others that are
going on with the iron-works." Pool forge, on the
Manatawny, belonged to Rutter. The patent of William Penn to Thomas Rutter was issued 17.14–15, for

three hundred acres on the main branch of the Manatawny, five miles above Pottstown. In 1717 Rutter
opened the Colebrookdale mines. It is fair to conclude
that there is little difference in priority between Ball,
Rutter, and Nutt, as to bar iron, and little doubt as to
Keith's priority in making pig iron, in territory then
belonging to Pennsylvania. Indeed, the enterprise of
Sir William Keith, though successful for so short a time,
was productive of the most beneficial results to the trade.
As soon as his furnace got into successful operation, it
was imitated by others, as Colonel Spottswood said, and
the bloomeries, wasteful and slow, converted into finery
forges, using pig iron. This change was made before
1730, and the bloomery process was never afterward
adopted to any extent in Pennsylvania. This fact distinguished the early Pennsylvania manufacture from that
of most of the other producing regions, since the greatest
part of its iron was made in forges.

King built a blast furnace in Lancaster county, in
1726, and the Durham Iron-works was built about 1727,
by a company, in which James Logan, James Hamilton,
and others were interested. A stone, apparently a
keystone, marked 1727, has been placed in the Cen-
tennial Exhibition by Cooper, Hewitt & Co., the present
owners. Logan wrote, in 1728, that there were then
four furnaces in blast in Pennsylvania.

On May 20th, 1728, we find Durham Iron-works
mentioned in the minutes of Council, in connection
with Indian troubles. Mr. Buck, in his history of
Bucks county, states that ore was shipped from Durham, down the Delaware, before the furnace was built.
This trade created a peculiar boat, with oars and sails,
called the "Durham boat." The Durham works were
the starting point whence three men, under Penn's

treaty, fixed the boundary of Pennsylvania, by a day's walk between sunrise and sunset. One of them walked to the crest of Pocono mountain, distancing the Indians as well as his companions. We find that the Grubb family began business in 1728, at Cornwall, where Peter Grubb discovered the iron-ore deposits, since proved to be of such vast extent. Colebrookdale furnace was built in 1734, by a company, in which Nat. French and Alex. Wooddrop owned a half, and Thomas Potts a twenty-fourth interest. The estimated cost was £500. Warwick furnace, on French creek, was built in 1736, by Anna Nutt and her sons, and Mount Pleasant furnace soon after, by Thomas Potts and his sons. The intermarriage of the Rutter and Savage heirs (females) with David, Thomas, and John Potts, brought the greater part of the iron-works of the Province into the hands of the Potts family. Mrs. Rebecca Nutt, widow of Samuel Nutt, Jr., married Robert Grace, who thus came (1745) into the management, along with John Potts, of the Coventry and Warwick properties. He was a man of means and high education, having spent three years in Europe studying metallurgy; and Peter Collinson wrote to John Bartram, in 1737, that Grace "will be able to give our friend Wolley some satisfaction as to the richness and quality of his ores." Grace aided Franklin materially, and was the mainstay of the Philadelphia Library in its early days.

In 1723 the owners of iron-works prayed the Assembly of the Province to prohibit the sale of liquors, except cider and beer, at retail, to their men. It expired, and in 1735 was re-enacted, in the following terms:—

"WHEREAS, The erecting of furnaces for running and melting iron-ore hath proved successful and advantageous to the trade of this Province in general, and if duly encouraged and improved will render our commerce with Great Britain of more esteem and our remittances more easy and beneficial to the inhabitants than the methods heretofore used;

"AND WHEREAS, The act against selling rum and other liquors hath been found useful and has now expired:

"*Be it enacted*, That no person shall, within a distance of three miles to any furnace now or hereafter to be erected in said Province, keep a public house, or sell, by permit or otherwise, any liquor or wine (except they be specially recommended, by license or permit, to the justices of the county by a majority of the owners of such iron-works), under penalty of forty shillings for each offense."

It would even now be advantageous could this very law be put in force. "Whisky-drinking and fox-hunting" were the banes of many an early forge, whisky has caused trouble from that day to this; and yet it is not a material at all necessary for making iron. The furnaces are not charged with it, and there is no good reason why the men should be. It is, however, a fair estimate to say, that for every ton of rails made at least a gallon of whisky and one of beer are consumed.— (D. J. Morrell, 1864.)

The Redding furnace was built in 1737, by Samuel Nutt and William Branson. Some inhabitants of Lancaster county petitioned (January 25th, 1737) "for a road from Lancaster to Coventry works, on French creek, and to the furnace called Redding's, now erecting on said creek." William Branson built a forge at Windsor, about 1738. The Cornwall furnace was built in 1742, by Peter Grubb, of Chester county, and *still remains in blast.* Its stack was then thirty-two feet high, twenty-one and one-half feet square at the base, and eleven feet at the top. In 1758 it made twenty-four tons a week. It passed into the hands of Robert Coleman, in 1798. Another Colebrookdale furnace was erected west of Cornwall, in 1745. The Elizabeth furnace, near Lititz, was built in 1756, probably by Benezet & Co. It was managed, in 1762, by Baron Steigel, a German nobleman of wealth. He was eccentric and extravagant, lived in a castle, and received his visitors with salvos of artillery and with music by his workmen, who stopped work for the purpose. He was a man of ability, however, and erected a glass-works; but when the Revolution cut him off from his German estates he failed and became superintendent for Robert Coleman.

The following forges, in addition to those above mentioned, were in operation before 1750, on the Manatawny and its branches:—Spring, Amity, a second Pool, Pine and Little Pine, and McCall's forges; Glasgow forge was built about 1759. On French creek we find Vincent's Steel-works, believed to have been in operation in 1734, and which went, in 1759, into the hands of William Branson. On the Perkiomen creek (twenty miles north of Norristown), Green Lane forge was built in 1733.

Further, in 1759, Acrelius mentions Sarum works, with three stacks, belonging to Taylor's heirs; Crum Creek works, bought by Peter Dicks, after it had ruined the Crosby family; and Dixon's works (a bloomery), in York county, also owned by Peter Dicks.

An example of the yields of the early furnaces is furnished by the records of the Mount Pleasant furnace, between October 12th, 1738 (its first blast) and July 20th, 1741. During this period it made seven blasts, the shortest being ten days, the longest being four months, less two days, and produced in all six hundred and ninety tons seventeen hundred weight two quarters and fifty-nine and one-quarter tons of pig iron. It produced an average of one and fifty-two one-hundredths tons per day worked, or about ten tons per week. This was a small furnace, because the Virginia furnaces made twenty tons per week in 1732; while Swedenborg estimates fifteen and three-quarter tons as the product of the Pennsylvania furnaces of 1734, and Grubb's furnace made twenty-five tons per week in 1750. William Allen stated to Acrelius, in 1759, that twenty to twenty-five tons per week was an average product in New Jersey, and Dr. Thatcher fixed the average product of a furnace in Massachusetts at seventeen and three-quarter tons per week. In those early times both furnaces and forges stopped during the four summer months.

In 1731 pig iron sold at the first Colebrookdale furnace for five pounds ten shillings, Pennsylvania currency (fourteen dollars and sixty-three cents). The Penn collections show that Baltimore and Principio pig iron was worth six pounds to six pounds ten shillings sterling in England, in 1736; and John Tomlin stated to Parliament that, in 1727, bar iron cost in New England twelve pounds five shillings to twelve pounds ten shillings sterling per ton, and the freight to England was two pounds sterling per ton.

(Acrelius gives the following account of the workmen and methods in use in 1759:—" The workmen are partly English and partly Irish, with some few Germans, though the work is carried on after the English method.) The pig iron is smelted into geese, and is cast from five to six feet long and a half foot broad, for convenience of forging, which is in the Walloon style. The pigs are first operated upon by the finers. Then the chiffery or hammer-men take it back again into their hands and beat out the long bars. The finers are paid thirty shillings a ton, the hammer-men twenty-three shillings ninepence per ton—that is to say, both together, two pounds thirteen shillings and ninepence sterling. * * * * The laborers are generally composed partly of negroes (slaves), partly of servants from Germany or Ireland bought for a term of years. A good negro is bought for thirty to forty pounds sterling. His clothing and food may amount to eight pounds sterling—very little indeed for the year. The negroes are better treated in Pennsylvania than anywhere else in America. A white servant costs seven pounds sterling, and his food is estimated at six pounds ten shillings sterling." Acrelius said that hickory charcoal was used as the best, then ash and white oak, but black-oak charcoal was most abundant.

We see that most of the Pennsylvania iron-works lay, in 1759, within a radius of forty miles from Philadelphia, and they all exported iron from Philadelphia, except Grubb, who sent his pig iron down the Susquehanna, whence it went to England with the Virginia and Maryland iron. Acrelius states the carriage paid on iron did not exceed twenty shillings sterling per ton, being reduced by the return loads of store goods. " Pig iron is sold at the furnaces for from three pounds six shillings eightpence to three pounds ten shillings sterling per ton. Bar iron at the forge brings twenty pounds sterling per ton, or twenty shillings per one hundred pounds. It is sold dear, for six months' credit is given. Pig iron is sold in Philadelphia at five pounds sterling per ton; bar iron, in large quantities, at from fourteen to sixteen pounds sterling per ton. It certainly seems remarkable that the price is diminished after the long transportation to the city; but in this people find their profit. Moulded goods or castings of kettles, stoves, etc., are sold at the furnace for five pounds six shillings eightpence sterling per ton; in Philadelphia for seven pounds six shillings eightpence sterling per ton."

During twenty-four years, between 1729 and 1748 (excluding, for want of records, 1736, 1737, and 1738), Pennsylvania exported two thousand four hundred and sixty-eight tons seven hundred pounds of pig and bar iron to England, and during six years, from 1750 to 1755, inclusive, four thousand eight hundred and seventy-two tons five hundred and four pounds of pig iron, and three hundred and thirteen tons two thousand one hundred pounds of bar iron.

In obedience to act of Parliament, of 1756, Governor Denny, of Pennsylvania, was desired, in 1757, by the Lords of Trade, to transmit "a just and true account of the quantity of iron made between Christmas, 1749 and June, 1756." We append his own summary of this report:—

	Tons.	Cwt.	Qrs.	Lbs.
Pine forge made in six years and twelve days, ...	747	12	8	6
Pool forge made in four years, ...	313	4	2	6
Glasgow forge made in five years three months and sixteen days, ...	595	7	0	0
Coventry forge made in seven years, ...	339	9	1	1
Helmstead forge made in seven years, ...	480	3	1	21
Windsor forge made in six years and twelve days, . .	495	14	3	5
Union forge (built 1750) made in six years, ...	332	7	1	0
Pottsgrove forge made in one year, ...	64	15	0	0
Total, ...	3378	13	3	11

Taking the average, we find that Pennsylvania then made not far from *four hundred and seventy tons of bar iron yearly.*

In accordance with the act of 1749, discouraging the manufacture of wrought iron and steel in America, Governor Hamilton, of Pennsylvania, issued the following proclamation :—

By the Honorable JAMES HAMILTON, ESQ., Lieutenant-Governor and Commander-in-Chief of the Province of Pennsylvania and Counties of New Castle, Kent, and Sussex, on Delaware.

A PROCLAMATION.

WHEREAS, By an Act of Parliament passed in the Twenty-third year of His Majesty's Reign, entitled *An Act to encourage the Importation of Pig and Bar Iron from his Majesty's Colonies in America, and to prevent the Erection of any Mill, or other Engine, for slitting or rolling of iron, or any plating-forge to work with a Tilt-Hammer, or any Furnace for making Steel in any of the said Colonies*, it is enacted—"That from and after the Twenty-fourth day of *June*, in the year of our Lord one Thousand Seven Hundred and Fifty, every Governor, Lieutenant-Governor, and Commander-in-Chief of any of His Majesty's Colonies in America, shall forthwith transmit to the Commissioners for Trade and Plantations, a Certificate, under his Hand and Seal of Office, containing a particular Account of every Mill or Engine for slitting and rolling of Iron, and every plating-forge to work with a Tilt-Hammer, and every Furnace for making Steel, at the Time of the Commencement of this Act, erected in his Colony; expressing, also, in the said Certificate, such of them as are used, and the name or names of the Proprietor or Proprietors of each such Mill, Engine, Forge, and Furnace, and the place where each such Mill, Engine, Forge, and Furnace is erected, and the number of Engines, Forges, and Furnaces in the said Colony." To the End, therefore, that I may be the better enabled to obey the Directions of said Act, I have thought fit, with the advice of the Council, to issue this Proclamation, hereby enjoining and requiring the Proprietor or Proprietors, or in case of their Absence, the Occupiers of any of the above-mentioned Mills, Engines, Forges, and Furnaces, erected within this Province, to appear before me, at the City of Philadelphia, on or before the Twenty-first day of September next, with proper and ample Testimonials of the Right of such Proprietor, Proprietors, and Occupiers therein, and sufficient Proofs whether the said Mills, Engines, Forges, and Furnaces respectively were used on the said Twenty-fourth Day of *June* or not: And I do further hereby require and command the Sheriff of every County in this Province respectively, on or before the said Twenty-first day of *September*, to appear before Me, at the City of *Philadelphia* aforesaid, and then and there by Writings, under their Hands and Seals, to certify and make known to Me, every Mill or Engine for slitting and rolling of Iron, every plating-forge to work with a Tilt-Hammer, and every Furnace for making Steel, which were erected within their several and respective Counties, on the said Twenty-fourth Day of *June*, and the Place and Places where the same were erected, with the names of their respective Proprietor or Proprietors, and the Occupiers of them, and every of them; and whether they or any of them were used on the said Twenty-fourth Day of June or not, as they and each of them will answer the contrary at their Peril.

GIVEN *under my Hand and the Great Seal of the Province of* Pennsylvania, *at* Philadelphia, *this Sixteenth Day of* August, *in the Twenty-fourth year of the Reign of our Sovereign Lord,* GEORGE *the Second, King of* Great Britain, France, *and* Ireland, *&c., and in* the year of our Lord 1750.

JAMES HAMILTON.

By His HONOR'S command.

RICHARD PETERS, Secretary.

GOD Save the KING.

PHILADELPHIA: Printed by B. FRANKLIN, Printer to the Province, MDCCL.

This proclamation the sheriffs answered as follows:—

Joseph Hart, high sheriff of Bucks county, 20th September, 1750—"No mills or engines or plating-forge or steel-furnace in Bucks county, on the 24th June last."

Andrew Work, sheriff of Lancaster county, 3d September, 1750—"No mill, engine, &c. therein."

John Owen, sheriff Chester county, 18th September, 1750—"No plating-forge nor steel-furnace, and only one mill for slitting and rolling iron, belonging to John Taylor, in Thornbury township, built in 1746, in use 24th June, 1750."

Richard Sewell, sheriff Philadelphia county, 24th September, 1750—"William Branson, in city of Philadelphia, furnace for making steel, 24th June, 1750; Stephen Paschall, in city of Philadelphia, furnace for making steel, 24th June, 1750; John Hall, in county of Philadelphia, plating-forge, with tilt-hammer, in township Bilberry, not in use during past twelve months."

Also, Stephen Paschall swears, September 18th, 1750, "Furnace for making steel, built in 1747, at north-west corner Walnut and Eighth streets, in good working order on 24th June, 1750; wood, coal, iron, converting ingredients, &c. being on hand. Property absolutely in me."

So there were only one slitting and rolling mill, one plating forge, and two steel-works in the Province of Pennsylvania a hundred and twenty-six years ago.

Peter Kalm, a Swedish naturalist, visited Pennsylvania, in 1748 passing some months in Philadelphia and vicinity. He wrote, in November, 1748, that so much iron was made in the colony that not only the inhabitants had plenty, but foreign ships were also stocked, and it was exported to the West Indies. The iron was considered better for shipbuilding than Swedish iron, because it did not rust so soon. Many persons thought they could send iron to England and sell it there lower than other nations, especially when the colony became more thickly settled and wages were, consequently, lowered.

The amount of iron exported from Philadelphia for the year ending April 5th, 1766, was eight hundred and eighty-two tons of bar iron, valued at twenty-six pounds sterling per ton, and eight hundred and thirteen tons of pig iron at seven pounds ten shillings, in the currency of the colony. There were also exported for the years 1771, 1772, and 1773 the following amounts of pig and bar iron taken together, viz., two thousand three hundred and fifty-eight, two thousand two hundred and five, and one thousand five hundred and sixty-four tons.

Some time before 1789 Samuel Potts prepared the following list of the iron-works then existing in the State:—

List of Furnaces in Pennsylvania.

				Tons.
Viz.:	1. Warwick,	.	.	. 1,200
	2. Hopewell,	.	.	. 700
	3. Durham,	.	.	. 400

Carried forward, 2,300

			Tons
	Brought forward,		2,300

Maryan.	4. German,	.	.	.	300
Codorus.	5. Oley,		.	.	200
Mastick.	6. Mount Pleasant,			.	50
Reading.	7. Rebecca,	.		.	400
Colebrookdale.	8. Berkshire,	.		.	500
Herryford.	9. Elizabeth,	.		.	500
	10. Cornwall,	.		.	500
	11. Mount Hope,		.		500
	12. Carlisle,	.		.	400
	13. Pine Grove,		.	.	200
	14. Chambers,		.	.	300

16)6,150(439

Forges.

Salford,	Glasgow,	Windsor,
Green Lane,	Pine,	T. Olds',
Valley,	Spring,	Martick,
Pennel,	Oley,	Speedwell,
Sarum,	Millgrove;	Hopewell,
Twaddles,	Mount Pleasant,	C. Grubb's,
Doe Run,	Fosh's,	Codorus,
Brandywine,	Birdsborough,	Spring,
More's,	Gibraltar,	Carlisle,
Vanleer's,	Mescalom,	Mountain,
Coventry,	Charming,	Chambers'.
Young's,		34 forges.

Thirty-six thousand bar; one thousand tons castings.

Persons employed in making iron in Pennsylvania, between ten thousand and twelve thousand; supposed to consume one hundred and thirty-two thousand bushels of grain.

Grain consumed by horses, eighty thousand bushels. £63,000 expended in grain. £100,500 produce of iron. Five thousand tons of pig iron.

NOTE.—The figures corresponding to the furnaces probably represent their capacity in tons, and the average of their total is four hundred and thirty-nine tons. It is clear that the "thirty-six thousand bar" means hundred weight, and one thousand eight hundred tons the product named. If two tons, as was probably the case, of pig were required to the ton of bar iron, then the totals of pig iron converted into bars *plus* that made into castings will nearly agree with the five thousand tons pig iron named. The second Spring forge was probably in York county.

In 1794, Tench Coxe stated in his View of the United States that "the slitting and rolling mills of Pennsylvania are ascertained to cut and roll one thousand five hundred tons or three million three hundred and sixty thousand pounds per annum, and so completely do they obviate the objection of manual labor which is urged against American manufacturers that they employ but twenty-five (25) hands. In that State there are also sixteen large furnaces and thirty-seven large forges * * It does not appear that any of the American States makes so large quantities of pig and bar iron as Pennsylvania, nor is there any State which appears to have in its bowels so much pit coal in situations favorable to manufactures of American productions and increased trade. It is estimated that, taking into calculation the extent and number of the existing furnaces and forges of Pennsylvania, the *new iron-works of the last seven years are equal to one-half of all those which have been erected in the State during and before the year 1787.*"

NORTH CAROLINA.

Sir Walter Raleigh obtained in April, 1584, a grant, as Lord Proprietor, of all the territory between the Santee and Delaware rivers. In July, 1584, the expedition he sent out touched at the islands Wocoken and Roanoke, explored the sounds, and brought back such glowing accounts that Queen Elizabeth regarded the discovery as the most glorious event in her reign.

Raleigh sent another expedition in 1585, which landed in August, 1585, on Roanoke island, to prepare for a permanent settlement. Ralph Lane, the governor, was accompanied by learned men, who were to explore the country. Harriot, in his "Brief and True Report of the new found land of Virginia," published in 1590, thus recounts the discovery of iron-ore, *the first record of such discovery in America:*—"Near the water at two places, fourscore and sixscore furlongs from the settlement, rocky ground was found, which, by the trial of the mine, was found to hold iron richly. It is found in many places of the country else. I know nothing to the contrary but that it may be allowed for a good merchantable commodity, considering there the small charge for the labour and finding of men, the infinite store of wood, the want of wood and dearnes thereof in England, and the necessity of ballasting ships." Three successive colonies were destroyed by famine and Indian warfare, and the necessity of self-preservation left no opportunity for practicing the arts. Virginia was finally settled further north, on the James, by other adventurers, and no iron was made in North Carolina till shortly before the Revolution.

In the Chatham belt of specular iron-ores several veins of considerable size crop out near the Gulf of

Deep river, and one of them forms Ore hill, three hundred feet high, in which the greatly thickened exposure of the vein traverses the talcose slates which form the knob. Here large masses of ore were extracted during the Revolution, and were probably used by John Wilcox, who had a furnace and forge in the vicinity, on Deep river, in operation at that time. There were other works near his in Guilford county. In April, 1776, the Congress of the Province sent Commissioners to obtain the use of both works for casting cannon and shot; the Guilford works needed repairs, and the commissioners were authorized to purchase or repair it, and to draw for £5000 to carry out their instructions.

The Danbury beds of magnetic ore were worked in Stokes county by several bloomeries during and after the Revolution; the Union Bloomery forge, near Martin's Lime Kilns, was built in 1780; Hill's Bloomery, on Tom's creek, nineteen miles west of Danbury, in 1791, and Keyser's bloomery, on Town Fork, ten miles south-west of Danbury, in 1796. These had been once rebuilt, and the first two were still in operation in 1859. The magnetic ores of Lincoln county were worked as early as 1795, the Vesuvius furnace on Anderson's creek, ten miles east of Lincolnton, having been built in 1795. In Surry county, settled in 1753, by Moravians from Pennsylvania, iron was made on the Yadkin river before the close of the last century.

In 1775 the Congress of the Province offered premiums to stimulate all kinds of manufactures. For the first and second rolling and slitting mills, provided they made and slit five tons of iron within two years, the sums of £250 and £200 were respectively offered. For the first steel-furnace which should within eighteen months make one ton of merchantable steel, as good as British steel, a premium of £100 was offered, and for the second £20. The sum of £500 was offered to any person who should build, within two years, a blast-furnace for the production of good pig iron and hollow ware. In 1776 commissioners in the principal iron districts were appointed to arrange for the manufactnre of muskets and bayonets, but the commissioners for the district of Hillsborough reported that iron fit for the purpose could not be had in the State. Hence it is evident that the iron trade of North Carolina dates from the Revolution.

TENNESSEE.

The pioneers to the territories west of North Carolina named the Appalachian range, on the western boundary of that province, the Great Iron Mountain. Such it is certainly entitled to be called, now that its vast treasures of magnetic and specular ores in the Unaka mountains, at Cranberry and elsewhere, have been exploited; but the early settlers did not work these ores to any great extent. They had come from Virginia by way of the Great Valley, and they worked the brown hematites so richly deposited along the base of the mountains. A bloomery was built in 1790, at Emoryville, eight miles south of Jonesboro; at Elizabethtown, on the Doe river, Carter & Co. built another bloomery in 1795; in that year Wagner's bloomery, on Roane's creek, near Taylorsville, started, and in the same year the Mossy creek and Dumpling bloomeries, near Dandridge, Jefferson county, came into existence. In Green county a bloomery was built about 1797, on Camp creek, south-east of Greenville. None of these are now in operation, though the Emoryville bloomery was converted into a rolling-mill, in 1833, called the Pleasant Valley works. Wagner's works made *three and a half tons* of bar iron in 1856. The Mossy creek and Dumpling forges were abandoned before 1815. The abandonment or establishment of one of these bloomeries involved no great loss or labor, and they sprang up and disappeared in large numbers during the first half of the present century.

Before the close of the last century David Ross built a furnace and forge on the North Fork of the Holston river, near the Virginia line; these lay on the National road from Knoxville to Philadelphia. Mr. Ross also owned works in Campbell county, Virginia. Boats of twenty-five tons could ascend to Ross' works, nearly one thousand miles above the mouth of the Tennessee and two hundred and eighty above Nashville. At Long Island, on the Holsten, not far above these works, the first permanent settlement in Eastern Tennessee had been made in 1775, and these boats carried iron and other products thence as far as New Orleans.

Nashville was founded in 1780, and a few years later iron-ore was discovered in the Mero district, some thirty miles below the town. About 1790, a blast-furnace was erected in this region, on the Iron Fork of Barton's creek, seven miles west of Charlotte, in Dickson county. This furnace is still in operation as the Cumberland charcoal-furnace. The rich iron-ore formations of Western Tennessee and Kentucky have supported a great number of charcoal-furnaces since that time. At one of them—the Suwannee—William Kelly carried on his experiments in refining pig iron in the hearth of the furnace, as we shall describe in connection with the history of Cambria county, Pennsylvania.

SOUTH CAROLINA.

The Huguenot colonies of 1562 and 1564, at Port Royal (Beaufort Island), perished through famine and Spanish massacres. Charles II. granted the territory south of Virginia, in 1663, to a company of eight of his friends,—among them General Monk, Ashley Cooper, Sir George Carteret, a proprietor of New Jersey, and Sir William Berkeley, governor of Virginia. In this grant several settlements already existed: on the Chowan river, the Albemarle county colony; and near Wilmington, the Clarendon county colony. In 1670 the proprietors founded a settlement on Beaufort Island, but removed it in 1671 to the old town below Charlestown. This colony was devoted to agriculture; conflicts with the Spaniards and Indians unsettled it till 1715, and the early introduction of slave labor rendered skilled workmen scarce and wages high. The bog-ore deposits on the coast are unimportant; but in the interior, in the north-western section, several considerable belts of specular and magnetic ore cross the State. It required some time, however, for the settlers to reach these, and the first iron-works was built only two years before the Revolution.

The magnetic ores are chiefly confined to a belt of slate, in the York, Union, and Spartanburg districts. which crosses Broad river at Cherokee ford, and extends along the northern side of King's mountain to the head of People's creek. The specular ores occur in a belt of mica slates overlying the former, and forming the northern slope of King's mountain, from the North Carolina line to Gelkey's mountain. A bed of the same slate, overlying the limestone of York district, also contained specular ore.

In this region, near King's mountain, Dr. Ramsay states that the first iron-works in the State was built by Mr. Buffington, in 1773. They were destroyed during the Revolution, the region becoming the scene of continued conflict,—the battles of King's mountain and Cowpens being fought in the iron-ore district itself.

In 1775 the Provincial Congress, feeling the necessity of a supply of iron, steel, and lead to the continuance of the war, offered £1000 for the erection of the first bloomery which should make one ton of good bar iron; £800 for the second, and £700 for the third bloomery. To each of the first three works which should produce five hundred pounds of good steel a reward of £500 was promised. A premium of £700 was set apart for the first slitting and rolling mill which should make a thousand pounds of nail-rods. The Confederate States pursued the same policy in the Civil War. By their direct aid the furnaces in the Spartanburg district (owned by one of the Moses family), the North Carolina and Tennessee forges and the Alabama works furnished a large part of the cast and wrought iron used subsequent to the commencement of the war.

After the Revolution, about the year 1787, two furnaces, the Era and the Etna, were built in York county, in Camden district, on a creek flowing into the Catawba, about ten miles west of that river, and on the road from Yorkville to Charlotte, North Carolina. They used surface ore, after roasting, and made pig iron for castings and hollow ware. The pig iron made good bar iron in the forge, and an attempt to convert the bar into steel met with some success. Mr. William Hill reinvented the *trompe*, with which "he blew all the fires, both of the forges and furnaces, so as to render unnecessary the use of wheels, cylinders, or any other kind of bellows."

These works had communication through Camden, eighty miles below, on the Wateree river. The owners proposed to open the navigation of the Wateree and Catawba for boats of thirty tons eighty miles beyond the North Carolina line. They obtained charters from South and North Carolina, and actually improved the navigation as an outlet for the product of their works. A canal was subsequently built along the river, which proved very useful to iron-works in North Carolina.

KENTUCKY.

The first settlement of Kentucky was made by Daniel Boone, at Boonesboro, in 1775. Born in Berks county, Pennsylvania, he had come by way of Yadkin, North Carolina, as he grew up, to the settlements on the Holston river. From these, he opened up a road to the Kentucky river through a wilderness, in which he was at home. No doubt the iron-works on the Holston supplied necessary munitions for the constant warfare in which he and his companions were engaged. Looking over the history of the early settlements it seems as if iron-works had been then held to be, what they have since proved themselves, the necessary base of a community that shall flourish in the arts or protect itself in war. The early works seem to have followed up or to have been the starting-point of each new departure into the wilderness.

The first iron-furnace in this State was built, while the region was nearly a wilderness, by Government troops, in 1791. It was named the Old Slate Charcoal furnace, and was located on the Slate Branch of Licking river, about five miles north-east of Owingsville. It ran on ore from the dolomite rocks of the upper

Silurian or Clinton group, and was finally abandoned in 1838.

Jefferson, in his "Notes on Virginia" (1781), wrote of the Western country, that "we are told of iron-mines between the Muskingum and the Ohio, and of others in Kentucky, between the Cumberland and Barren rivers; between Cumberland and Tennessee, on Ready creek, near the Long Island, and on Chestnut creek, a branch of the great Kanahwa, near where it crosses the Carolina line. What are called the Iron Banks, on the Mississippi, are believed, by a good judge, to have no iron in them. In general, from what is hitherto known of that country, it seems to want iron."

How little Jefferson knew of the buried riches of the regions he thus described! The great lower Silurian brown hematite deposits of the East Tennessee valley, and the upper Silurian fossil red hematite, in large beds to the north-west in the valley, have both been largely developed. The Hanging Rock or Ironton region of Ohio and Kentucky has supported in its palmy days more than seventy charcoal-furnaces, using the coal-measure carbonates of the district; and there are now forty-four furnaces in it. In Western Kentucky and Tennessee, south-west of the western coal-field of Kentucky, an iron region, a hundred and twenty-five miles long by fifty wide, lies along the Cumberland river, as an undulating plateau, much cut up by water-courses. Rich deposits exist over the whole district, forming, in many instances, the ridges between the streams, and some of these ore-banks exhibit a thickness of fifty to two hundred feet of ore overlying limestone. The ore is all brown hematite, of the honeycomb, pipe, and pot varieties. In 1854 forty charcoal-furnaces in blast in this region made fifty-one thousand two hundred and seventeen tons of pig iron, though there are now only sixteen furnaces altogether.

NEW HAMPSHIRE.

In this State so-called iron ore was discovered at an early date, according to the following letter of Mr. Gibbons, quoted by Dr. Belknap. In 1634, Mr. Gibbons shipped to his principal in England specimens of ore from the vicinity of Portsmouth, with the remark that "there is of three sorts—one sort that the mine doth cast forth as the tree doth gum," and that one of the other sorts was rich and the deposit extensive. Douglass, in his "Summary of British Settlements," mentions a "noted iron-works at Lamper-Eel river," which used bog ore, but was soon discontinued. Probably the first pig iron made in the State was smelted at Furnace Village, from the magnetic ore of Winchester, by a company of Rhode Island men,—Hawkins, Jenks, Arnold, Cahoon, and others,—in 1795. Iron-works of some kind existed in Exeter before that date. The Franconia Iron Company was incorporated in 1805; it smelted the Franconia ore in a small charcoal furnace, built in 1811, which was rebuilt in 1844 with hot blast, and a new furnace was erected in 1859, which has since been abandoned. No pig iron is now made in New Hampshire.

VERMONT.

The principal locality of the iron manufacture of the State was in Bennington. The ore is mostly brown hematite, of the lower Silurian formations; the magnetic ores of the State have never been successfully worked. A number of forges were built before the territory separated from New Hampshire, in 1791. In Tinmouth,

Rutland county, a mine, perhaps the Chipman bed, was worked in 1785, and in 1798 there were ten or twelve forges in the township. The old Granger furnace, once of the Pittsford Iron Company, now belonging to Mr. J. Pritchard, was built about 1791, on Furnace river, which empties into Otter creek, near Centre Rutland; it was rebuilt in 1824, size eight by twenty-seven feet, and enlarged in 1853 to nine feet by forty-two feet high. It was blown by two cylinders sixty-six inches diameter and fifty-one inches stroke, driven at three revolutions a minute by a water-wheel twenty-four feet in diameter. It ran either hot or cold, and in 1859 its capacity was about eight tons a day, the blasts usually commencing in July and ending in January or February.

In the eastern part of Bennington there are several beds of brown hematite. Alfred Hager said, in 1861, there were several old furnaces gone to decay, about the history of which little could be learned, but one could plainly see that a great deal of money had been needlessly wasted.

The Dorset furnace, a very old one, is principally remarkable for the following circumstance. In 1820, the manager of the furnace, Mr. Trenner, found a deposit of black oxide of manganese, and thinking it a very pure rich iron ore, put a large quantity of it into the furnace to get better iron. "But when the furnace was tapped the liquid stream took fire and burned with fury in all directions, driving all hands from the building, so that it was not possible to proceed till the manganese was removed from the furnace, at no little expense."

In Brandon, Rutland county, brown hematite ore was discovered in 1810; a forge was built soon afterward, and in 1820 John Conant built a furnace, which he conducted successfully, making car-wheel iron, till he sold it, in

1850, with about twenty-six hundred acres of land, to the Brandon Iron and Car-Wheel Company. Such had been the ill success of the Vermont furnaces that the enterprise was regarded as extremely hazardous. But in its later as well as earlier management it has been uniformly successful.

OHIO.

Ohio, though starting late, is certainly destined to a place in the front rank of the iron trade. Her domain was first put under a territorial government in 1787, on the 11th of July. The Mahoning region was settled in 1798, but was far from the regions then producing iron, and the high cost of carriage made that metal both scarce and dear, bar iron being brought on horseback from the Centre county district, in Pennsylvania. On the authority of Colonel Whittlesey, of Cleveland, it is stated that Glendenin, Montgomery, and Mackay, of Youngstown, built the first furnace in Ohio, in 1808, on the Mahoning, at the mouth of Yellow creek. The furnace was eight feet across the boshes and thirty-five feet high, built, like the early furnaces, against a bluff. It was a cold-blast charcoal-furnace driven by water-power, and produced only one and a half to two tons of pig iron per day. Its ruins may still be seen a short distance below the Mount Nebo mine. On the same authority, James Heaton is said to have built, in 1809, a finery forge on Musquito creek, at the place where Niles now stands; he used the iron of the Yellow creek furnace, and produced the first hammered bars in the State. On the other hand it is claimed in the "American Pioneer," that Moses Dillon, one of the builders of the Union furnace on Dunbar creek, in Fayette county, Pennsylvania, built a forge, at the end of the last century, on the Licking river, near Zanesville, probably the first in Ohio. The date at which Dillon left the Union furnace sustains this view. The later history of the Mahoning furnaces will be touched upon in the description of the Shenango valley of Pennsylvania.

GENERAL REVIEW.

We have thus brought the local history of the iron trade of the colonies to the close of its first epoch—the Revolution. It was a period in which our iron trade was really independent of foreign markets, and if permitted could readily have controlled the English market. Evelyn, one of the Lords of Trade, only used the language of the iron-men of his time, in speaking of the colonies as the source from which, in some shape or other, they must draw their future supply of iron. English merchants then began iron-making in America as a source of profit; the colonists carried it on as a means of strength and existence. They needed nails and bolts to build houses and ships, and made pig iron as a means of paying their debts in England.

The colonies, however, pursued the manufacture in very different ways. The first iron was made in Virginia, but only a few tons; New England began a persistent series of efforts to make iron as a raw material for her manufactures, and though this design unfortunately failed for want of ore, yet the work was not in vain. She built up many furnaces for castings, and her men established the iron trade of the northern colonies, meeting the southern iron-men in New Jersey. One of the Leonards, of Plymouth, doubtless assisted Colonel Morris, in East Jersey. The Virginian furnaces were successful, and were copied by Sir William Keith, when he became governor of Pennsylvania. Pennsylvania iron-men crossed into New Jersey, in the vicinity of Easton; among others, William Allen, chief justice of Pennsylvania, who owned the Union Iron-works.

The New England iron was made principally in forges, and it is interesting to note the completeness of the early works,—*a furnace and forge and not a bloomery only*. John Winthrop, Jr., the leader in these enterprises, was a man of great learning and executive ability. The New Jersey works included both bloomeries and forges, but comparatively few of the former (four in 1759), till the rich magnetic ores began to be worked. In Pennsylvania the bloomeries were abandoned at a very early date; the bloomery process was not considered satisfactory, although one bloomery (Dixon's) in York county was running in Acrelius' time. In Virginia bloomeries were apparently never used; but Virginia soon ceased to make bar iron, that being principally produced in Maryland, in forges.

The blowing apparatus of the furnaces and forges consisted of large double bellows, driven by water-power, the motion communicated by a cam arrangement on the water-wheel shaft. Wooden blowing-tubs, of short stroke, about three feet, were introduced not long before the Revolution. The blast furnaces all had a single tuyere only, rarely two, till about fifty years ago. About that time (1837), the owners of a furnace in the Middle States prided themselves on having the first blast furnace with *three tuyeres*.

The locality of the early manufacture was along the coast, or not far from it, and near navigable rivers. It was not till near the Revolution that the works reached the Alleghenies, and passed them first in Pennsylvania,—the first Fayette county furnace being built in 1777. Works were gradually built southward and westward down the Great Valley, along the main ridge of the Alleghenies, till they were passed in Tennessee, by the erection of a furnace in 1790.

Pennsylvania and Maryland produced more bar iron than any other colonies, and Maryland was the first to export bar iron, while Virginia was the first to export pig iron to England. Virginia, Maryland, and Pennsylvania supplied the Massachusetts forges largely with pig iron, and while Pennsylvania exported iron to the West Indies also, the Southern colonies sent theirs mainly to England.

The imports of the different colonies agree with this description of their manufacture. As to the amounts imported, our figures are all derived from reports submitted to committees of Parliament, which sat in 1719, 1736, and 1739, to inquire into the necessity of encouraging the importation of colonial pig iron into Great Britain. I append Scrivenor's tables of *Imports* into the colonies, as quoted by French. Scrivenor copied them from the originals in the House of Lords, which have been burnt, and they were surreptitiously published in the *London Mining Journal* for 1840. The table quoted by French is evidently incorrect, as it disagrees with Scrivenor's *averages* for the respective periods. I am unable to correct the quantities, as the whole publication has been abstracted from the only set of the *Mining Journal* to be found. The table is, however, an interesting one, in throwing light on the proportions taken by different colonies. In the fifteen years for which reports were submitted there were imported five thousand three hundred and twenty-one (5321) tons and twenty-two hundred and sixteen pounds of bar iron, and eighteen thousand five hundred and eighty-nine (18,589) tons two thousand and thirty pounds of iron wares (nails, cast-iron utensils, tools, &c.). Of the bar iron New England took over seventy-five (75.2) per cent., Virginia and Maryland about two (2.1), and Pennsylvania less than two (1.7) per cent. Of the iron wares Virginia and Maryland took over twenty-eight (28.4) per cent., New England about twenty-three (23.5) per cent., and Pennsylvania less than six (5.6) per cent. Hence it appears Colonel Spottswood was right in saying that Pennsylvania could manufacture her own iron for herself. It is equally clear that New England manufactured for others both her own and the imported bar iron, and was very persistent in maintaining both her right to do so and to ship her wares to other colonies.

Scrivenor states the *average* imports as follows, representing a total of thirty-six thousand nine hundred and seventy-six (36,976) tons; and a comparison will show the inaccuracy of the table immediately following. I have used the tables of Alexander to supply several gaps. Joshua Gee, writing in 1738, stated that about one-half of these imports consisted of *nails and spikes* of various kinds:—

Imports of Iron into American Plantations.

Years.					Tons.
1711 to 1718, average	.	.	.	.	1,732
1729 to 1738, average	.	.	.	.	2,312

Bar Iron and Iron Wares Imported by the American Colonies from 1710 to 1735.

	COLONIES.	IRON WARES.			BAR IRON.			
		Cwt.	Qrs.	Lbs.	Tons.	Cwt.	Qrs.	Lbs.
1711.	Carolina, ...	1,143	0	27	...	...	...	...
	New England, ...	4,596	2	16	200	3	0	7
	New York, ...	567	0	19	10	2	1	10
	Pennsylvania, ...	937	2	0	12	0	2	21
	Virginia and Maryland, . .	3,014	0	8	1	10	1	1
1712.	Carolina, ...	1,551	0	7	4	13	0	0
	New England, ...	5,344	3	24	281	13	3	19
	New York, ...	639	1	7	32	3	0	0
	Pennsylvania, ...	540	0	20	2	1	0	0
	Virginia and Maryland, . .	5,653	2	4	5	3	2	4
1713.	Carolina, ...	1,406	2	2	27	5	0	0
	New England, ...	983	0	13	212	1	0	0
	New York, ...	4,885	2	21	49	8	2	16
	Pennsylvania, ...	1,040	0	9	7	4	3	26
	Virginia and Maryland, . .	2,859	2	21	8	5	2	4
1714.	Carolina, ...	1,051	1	18	8	10	0	0
	New England, ...	4,633	0	3	279	6	3	0
	New York, ...	1,136	3	15	98	7	0	18
	Pennsylvania, ...	923	2	1	24	12	0	7
	Virginia and Maryland, . .	6,597	2	12	8	5	0	0
1715.	Carolina, ...	691	0	21	1	18	0	0
	New England, ...	5,795	2	24	372	10	1	0
	New York, ...	1,379	3	0	110	10	0	0
	Pennsylvania, ...	987	3	4	8	5	0	0
	Virginia and Maryland, . .	8,946	3	15	16	7	0	0
1716.	Carolina, ...	670	1	7	...	...	...	...
	New England, ...	5,397	2	2	372	10	3	0
	New York, ...	1,094	0	14	147	0	0	0
	Pennsylvania, ...	962	2	0	10	0	0	0
	Virginia and Maryland, . .	7,446	0	22	8	10	0	0

Bar Iron and Iron Wares Imported by the American Colonies from 1710 to 1735.—(Continued.)

	COLONIES.	IRON WARES.			BAR IRON.			
		Cwt.	Qrs.	Lbs.	Tons.	Cwt.	Qrs.	Lbs.
1717.	Carolina, ...	866	1	11	4	2	0	0
	New England, ...	3,819	6	5	140	7	0	0
	New York, ...	1,146	1	0	42	14	1	0
	Pennsylvania, ...	1,149	0	26	8	16	2	0
	Virginia and Maryland, . .	8,728	1	27	3	3	0	0
1718.	Carolina, ...	970	2	21	2	0	0	0
	New England, ...	3,110	1	1	154	4	0	0
	New York, ...	1,396	1	20	2	18	2	0
	Pennsylvania, ...	887	0	2	3	10	0	0
	Virginia and Maryland, . .	6,734	2	3	26	10	3	0
1729.	Carolina, ...	1,342	1	21	3	10	0	0
	New England, ...	7,393	3	0	337	12	2	23
	New York, ...	1,903	2	23	58	1	0	25
	Pennsylvania, ...	851	0	14	4	0	0	0
	Virginia and Maryland, . .	4,866	0	23	1	1	0	0
1730.	Carolina, ...	1,479	3	23	5	10	0	0
	New England, ...	7,329	2	24	149	13	1	5
	New York, ...	2,775	0	0	91	10	2	13
	Pennsylvania, ...	2,628	3	0	...	...	...	...
	Virginia and Maryland, . .	6,389	2	24	2	9	0	0
1731.	Carolina, ...	1,770	0	11	10	18	0	7
	New England, ...	9,727	1	7	243	8	2	7
	New York, ...	2,627	2	7	101	11	1	0
	Pennsylvania, ...	2,946	0	9	5	0	0	0
	Virginia and Maryland, . .	9,681	3	11	3	18	0	0
1732.	Carolina, ...	2,167	3	7	9	0	0	0
	Georgia, ...	291	0	0	...	...	...	...
	New England, ...	8,597	2	4	413	5	2	0
	New York, ...	2,380	0	24	58	5	3	27
	Pennsylvania, ...	2,207	2	26	2	14	0	0
	Virginia and Maryland, . .	7,445	3	27	4	14	0	0

Bar Iron and Iron Wares Imported by the American Colonies from 1710 to 1735.—(Continued.)

	COLONIES.	IRON WARES.			BAR IRON.			
		Cwt.	Qrs.	Lbs.	Tons.	Cwt.	Qrs.	Lbs.
1733.	Carolina, ...	2,692	3	11	25	0	0	0
	New England, ...	7,104	3	17	378	4	0	0
	New York, ...	1,609	3	7	55	0	0	0
	Pennsylvania, ...	2,419	2	0	2	0	0	0
	Virginia and Maryland, . .	8,815	1	10	12	0	0	0
1734.	Carolina, ...	2,880	2	19	25	0	0	0
	Georgia, ...	332	1	0	...	...	...	...
	New England, ...	7,104	3	14	370	14	2	0
	New York, ...	1,609	3	7	55	0	0	0
	Pennsylvania, ...	2,419	2	8	2	0	0	0
	Virginia and Maryland, . .	8,815	1	10	12	0	0	0
1735.	Carolina, ...	3,353	1	23	5	19	0	0
	Georgia, ...	1,700	0	0	4	0	0	0
	New England, ...	6,543	2	23	107	9	3	0
	New York, ...	2,136	2	0	108	8	1	5
	Pennsylvania, ...	2,102	0	0	...	...	...	...
	Virginia and Maryland, . .	9,709	12	4	2	13	0	0

The exports of iron from the colonies to England were exceedingly large, considering the extent of the production, and very interesting in the light of the policy of Parliament, during the eighteenth century. We find that Virginia, Maryland, and Pennsylvania exported in sixteen years (between 1761 and 1776) thirty-nine thousand two hundred and twenty-two tons nine hundred and seventy pounds of pig iron, and sixteen thousand two hundred and eighty-eight tons one thousand one hundred and two pounds of bar iron. These figures rest on the authority of British records, partly those of committees, partly of the Lords of Trade, quoted by Scrivenor and Alexander, but they probably represent the total export of the American colonies at too low a figure. They give the total pig iron exported to Great Britain from 1717 to 1776, from all colonies, as ninety-five thousand five hundred and seventy-seven tons two thousand and two pounds of pig and seventeen thousand seven hundred and twenty-six tons eight hundred and thirty-one pounds of bar iron, a total of one hundred and thirteen thousand three hundred and four ($113,304\frac{595}{2240}$) tons five hundred and ninety-five pounds. Scrivenor, however, from an examination of the same documents, gives one hundred and twenty-three thousand five hundred and sixty-four (123,564) tons as the general total; and Lord Sheffield, in his "Observations on the Commerce of the American States," says, that the average total amount exported by all the colonies in 1768, 1769, and 1770 was, yearly, two thousand five hundred and ninety-two tons bar iron, four thousand six hundred and twenty-four tons pig iron, and twelve tons of cast ware; that is, a total of twenty-one thousand six hundred and eighty-four tons in three years against sixteen thousand and seventy-three tons four hundred and fifty-five pounds stated below for the same period. Hence, we estimate that the total export of all the colonies was at least one hundred and fifty thousand (150,000) tons for the sixty years above mentioned.

EXPORTS OF IRON FROM THE AMERICAN PLANTATIONS.

(*Scrivenor.*)

Years.	Tons.
1717 and 1718, together, ...	7
1729 to 1735, average, ...	2,111
1739 to 1748, average, ...	2,423
1750 to 1755, average, ...	3,305
1761 to 1776, average, ...	4,045

Pig and Bar Iron Exported to Great Britain by the American Colonies from 1710 to 1736.

COLONIES.	LONDON.			OUTPORTS.		
	Tons.	Cwt.	Qrs.	Tons.	Cwt.	Qrs.
1718. Virginia and Maryland, ...	.	.	.	*3	7	0
1728–29. Pennsylvania, ...	99	13	2	174	12	3
Virginia and Maryland, ...	344	9	0	508	6	3
1730. Pennsylvania, ...	105	16	0	83	0	0
Virginia and Maryland, ...	779	17	0	746	17	0
1731. Pennsylvania, ...	88	1	0	81	1	0
Virginia and Maryland, ...	1,367	15	0	713	6	0
1732. Pennsylvania, ...	52	11	0	54	0	0
Virginia and Maryland, ...	1,504	8	0	721	0	0
1733. Pennsylvania, ...	43	3	0	52	0	0
Virginia and Maryland, ...	1,669	14	0	639	17	0
1734. Pennsylvania, ...	59	4	0	88	0	0
Virginia and Maryland, ...	1,397	17	0	644	4	0
1735. Pennsylvania, ...	197	14	0	44	17	0
"	.	.	.	*19	17	0
Virginia and Maryland, ...	1,353	3	0	1,059	0	0
Totals, ...	9,063	5	2	5,633	5	.2

* Bar iron.

These returns are from 1710; but no imports were made into Great Britain till 1718. They consist almost entirely of pig iron.

The duty on bar iron per ton was two pounds one shilling six and fifteen one-hundredths pence sterling.

The duty on pig iron per ton was three shillings nine and forty-five one-hundredths pence sterling.

No printed returns were made from 1719 to 1728, inclusive, nor for 1736 to 1738, inclusive.

Pig and Bar Iron Exported from the Colonies to Great Britain from 1739 to 1748.

YEARS.	PIG IRON.				BAR IRON.			
	Tons.	Cwt.	Qrs.	Lbs.	Tons.	Cwt.	Qrs.	Lbs.
1739. Pennsylvania, ...	170	5	0	0	44	9	0	0
Virginia and Maryland, . .	2,242	2	2	14	. . . .
1740. Pennsylvania, ...	159	0	0	0	. . . .
Virginia and Maryland, . .	2,020	2	0	22	5	0	0	0
1741. Pennsylvania, ...	153	0	0	0	. . . .
Virginia and Maryland, . .	3,261	8	1	5	5	0	0	0
1742. Pennsylvania, ...	143	0	0	0	. . . .
Virginia and Maryland, . .	1,926	3	1	5	. . . .
1743. Pennsylvania, ...	62	12	0	0	. . . .
Virginia and Maryland, . .	2,816	1	1	15	57	0	0	0
1744. Pennsylvania, ...	87	15	0	0	85	0	0	0
Virginia and Maryland, . .	1,748	4	1	3	. . . .
1745. Pennsylvania, ...	97	7	0	0	. . . .
Virginia and Maryland, . .	2,130	16	1	10	4	5	2	14
1746. Pennsylvania, ...	103	1	0	0	. . . .
Virginia and Maryland, . .	1,729	1	0	2	193	8	3	12
1747. Pennsylvania, ...	24	14	0	0	. . . .
Virginia and Maryland, . .	2,119	0	3	24	82	11	2	11
1748. Pennsylvania, ...	114	10	0	0	. . . .
Virginia and Maryland, . .	2,017	11	3	10	. . . .
Totals, ...	23,123	16	0	26	476	15	0	9

For 1749 no return was made.

Pig and Bar Iron Exported to Great Britain by. the American Colonies from 1750 to 1756.

COLONIES.	PIG IRON.			BAR IRON.		
	Tons.	Cwt.	Qrs.	Tons.	Cwt.	Qrs.
1750. Carolina, ...	. . . .			. . . .		
New England, ...	21	1	12	. . . .		
New York, ...	75	12	1	. . . .		
Pennsylvania, ...	318	9	3	. . . .		
Virginia and Maryland, . . .	2,508	16	1	5	17	3
1751. Carolina, ...	17	4	0	. . . .		
New England, ...	9	14	0	. . . .		
New York, ...	33	0	3	. . . .		
Pennsylvania, ...	199	15	0	. . . .		
Virginia and Maryland, . . .	2,950	5	3	3	4	2
1752. Carolina, ...	20	0	0	. . . .		
New England, ...	. . . .			. . . .		
New York, ...	41	5	0	. . . .		
Pennsylvania, ...	156	8	2	64	16	2
Virginia and Maryland, . . .	2,762	8	0	16	10	2
1753. Carolina, ...	10	0	6	. . . .		
New England, ...	40	10	0	2	8	0
New York, ...	97	4	3	. . . .		
Pennsylvania, ...	242	2	15	107	13	2
Virginia and Maryland, . . .	2,347	9	2	97	16	0
1754. Carolina, ...	20	0	0	. . . .		
New England, ...	4	16	0	. . . .		
New York, ...	115	16	2	6	10	0
Pennsylvania, ...	512	19	3	110	9	3
Virginia and Maryland, . . .	2,591	4	3	153	15	1
1755. Carolina, ...	14	0	3	. . . .		
New England, ...	. . . .			. . . .		
New York, ...	457	8	0	11	12	0
Pennsylvania, ...	836	6	1	79	5	0
Virginia and Maryland, . . .	2,132	15	1	299	1	3
Totals, ...	18,536	2	0	959	2	2

Pig and Bar Iron Exported by the American Colonies to Great Britain from 1760 to 1776.

YEAR.	PIG IRON.				BAR IRON.			
	Tons.	Cwt.	Qrs.	Lbs.	Tons.	Cwt.	Qrs.	Lbs.
1761, ...	2,766	2	3	12	39	1	0	0
1762, ...	1,763	6	0	2	122	12	2	14
1763, ...	2,566	8	0	25	310	9	3	2
1764, ...	2,554	8	3	21	1,059	8	0	10
1765, ...	3,264	8	1	22	1,078	16	0	16
1766, ...	2,887	5	1	15	1,257	14	3	9
1767, ...	3,323	2	1	19	1,325	19	0	18
1768, ...	2,953	0	2	14	1,989	11	0	16
1769, ...	3,401	12	2	9	1,779	13	0	23
1770, ...	4,232	18	1	18	1,716	8	0	21
1771, ...	5,303	6	3	13	2,222	8	1	24
1772, ...	3,724	19	2	11	965	15	0	23
1773, ...	2,937	13	0	23	837	3	3	16
1774, ...	3,451	12	2	14	639	2	0	23
1775, ...	2,996	0	2	16	916	5	2	11
1776, ...	316	1	3	8	28	0	1	8
Totals, ...	39,222	8	2	18	16,288	9	3	10

Now, while this progress was achieved in America, precisely the reverse took place in England. In that country the product of pig iron and bar had steadily diminished, through the destruction of the woods without replanting. From twenty-five thousand tons of pig iron and eighteen thousand tons of bar iron made in 1718, the product had diminished to twelve thousand tons bar iron in 1738, many of the furnaces being out and rendered useless by the importation of Swedish *bar iron*. In Surrey, about 1718, it cost over seven pounds sterling for wood to convert ore into pig, and in Sweden wood cost nothing. In 1717 a rupture with Sweden had cut off the supply of her iron for two years, and owing to inability to make the deficient quantity herself, England was forced to import it from Spain, Holland, Denmark, and Russia. Sweden discriminated against English ships, laid high duties on English goods, and prohibited the importation of some kinds. The balance of trade was stated by Mr. Harrison to be £120,000 against England. The Swedes had originally gained control of the market by strict attention to the quality of their iron, and as they did not know how to "perfect it themselves, and were obliged to ship it to Dantzig for that purpose," they procured workmen from Germany, in the seventeenth century, to teach them.

Peter the Great devoted close attention to fostering the iron trade of his country. With his sanction Count Demidoff built (1701) the Neviamski works in the Ural mountains. The furnaces were large, forty-five feet high, and made iron with only one hundred and fifteen to one hundred and seventy pounds of charcoal to one hundred pounds of iron. They worked rich magnetic ores, rather silicious, and made *white* pig iron for forges, and if the iron happened to be too gray they turned the tuyure down on the metal and refined it in the furnace hearth. Each furnace made thirty-five tons a week, being blown by powerful bellows, thirty-feet long by seven feet wide at their widest part. It was not long before this energetic management materially injured the sale of Swedish iron, and in 1769 Russia sent thirty-four thousand tons of iron to England.

The iron made in England during the eighteenth century was divided into two classes, *cold-short* and *tough*. The cold-short ore was got on the east side of the Severn, in the counties of Salop, York, Stafford, Nottingham, Chester, and Derbyshire. This kind of

iron was used only for nails, and sold at Bewdley for
£12 5s. to £13 5s. It was worked easily by the smiths,
and corresponded in character with the iron then imported from Russia. The ore that yielded tough iron
was won in the Cleehills, in Shropshire, in the Forest
of Dean, and in part of Wales, but principally in Cumberland. From the latter county it was carried to furnaces
in Lancashire, Hampshire, Yorkshire, Cheshire, Staffordshire, Gloucestershire, Worcestershire, and Shropshire.
The Cleehill iron was famous for musket-barrels, and
the Forest of Dean for scythes, since, though not very
tough, it welded kindly to steel and worked easily.
The Cumberland iron was soft when cold, sound when
hot, and exceedingly tough, and therefore most valuable,
especially when punched, bent, or worked cold. These
tough brands sold at £15 10s. to £16 per ton at Bewdley,
which town, in Worcestershire, was, in 1740, the centre
of the iron trade of England, the great market for iron of
all kinds. Swedish iron was the standard brand and
brought the highest price, the Orgroon (Dannemora)
iron being the best grade; but as it was rather hard
and of a steely nature it would not work cheaply into
nails, like the cold-short iron, and was excelled for
many purposes by the best variety of English tough
iron, though steel was long made almost exclusively of
it. I adduce these details as they are very important in
explaining English feelings concerning iron-making in
the colonies.

About the middle of the eighteenth century pig iron,
made in Monmouthshire and Breconshire, cost £4 10s.,
according to Mr. Octavius Morgan, a Welsh iron-
master, and substantially as much in other parts of the
kingdom. It was made from the weathered outcrop of
the coal-measure carbonate beds,—three tons of ore

making a ton of iron on the average. The ore was mined at 1s. 6d., and carried to the furnace in bags, on horses, at an average cost of about 5 shillings, a horse carrying two and a half hundred weight. Eighteen sacks of charcoal, containing eight bushels each (one sack being a horse-load), were used to the ton of iron; two of the sacks were used to calcine the ore. The cord of wood (9 feet long by 4 feet 6 inches high and 2 feet 2 inches in the billet) cost 1s. 6d. for cutting, in all 3s. 6d. per cord, and four cords made a load, or twelve (12) sacks of charcoal. The cost of coaling was five shillings, and the carriage, from one to fifteen miles to the furnace, was about eight (8) shillings per load. The repairs included new hearths and leathering the bellows. The furnaces made eight hundred (800) tons in one year, at the rate of about twenty-four (24) tons a week, but lay idle the whole of the next year to get stock. The furnace rent was £50 per year, and a blast required about £3000 worth of stock, so that the charge for interest amounted, for the two years, to 10 shillings per ton.

Cost of Iron in England.

	£	s.	d.
Three tons ore, ...	1	1	3
Limestone, 10 per cent., ...		1	3
Charcoal, 144 bushels, ...	2	10	0
Workmen and clerk's wages, . . .		5	0
Repairs, ...		2	6
Charge for interest, ...		10	0
Total, ...	4	10	0

This iron sold for £6 10 shillings per ton at that time, while American pig iron sold for £6, and was sent to

England at £4 10 shillings, or less than it cost to make iron there, the cost in Virginia being somewhere between two and three pounds sterling.

The product of Great Britain had decreased largely from the beginning of the century, and in 1738 was one-third less (twelve thousand tons bar iron) than it had been in 1718 (eighteen thousand tons bar iron). There were one hundred and twenty-five (125) forges in England in 1738; thirty of them lay idle and the rest made less than two-thirds of their usual product. The product of manufactured wares (nails, &c.) had increased, but the export had not kept pace with the manufacture and the trade was paralyzed. Men were discharged at Birmingham and became riotous. Though the exports to the colonies had undoubtedly increased, yet they could not take nor pay for enough to relieve the English works, and still the import of Swedish iron continued undiminished. It was brought in Swedish ships, paid for in cash, and the money was mostly spent in France.

England had, therefore, many reasons for encouraging iron-making in the colonies. Independence of foreign supply, a new market, and a grudge against Sweden, were powerful incentives. On the other hand, it was feared that, if successful, the colonies might injure or destroy the English trade. It was acknowledged that Great Britain could, in a few years, be entirely supplied with iron by the colonies, which were capable of making ten times as much as they could themselves consume. The number of forges and bloomeries was already so great that they conld not be destroyed, while wages of some kinds were high enough to induce skilled men to emigrate. A nail manufacturer at Middletown, Connecticut, wrote to Birmingham for three or four nailers, saying they could earn ten shillings a day, which would pay a week's board. The colonial works could get "pit coal," as ballast, for little more than it cost in England. Mr. Dulany, of Baltimore, bought a lot of coal at Annapolis, in 1738, and found he could "keep a fire with it as cheap as with wood." So the works on the coast either had coal cheap enough for use, to reheat their blooms and anchonies for drawing out, or could readily do without it.

Great Britain consumed about fifty thousand tons of bar iron, and imported the difference between her product and her consumption from Sweden, Russia, and Spain, over twenty thousand tons being drawn from Sweden, including one thousand two hundred to one thousand five hundred tons yearly for steel. The English manufacturer was mainly confined to refining the pig into bar iron, for there was not wood enough left to make both pig and bar iron, and coal could not then be used either in the furnace or in the forge, except for reheating. A supply of pig iron was, therefore, needed to enable the English forges to make cheap bar iron. Taking advantage of this situation, the British merchants imported a small quantity for trial in 1717, and petitioned for the removal of the duty. Small as the quantity was, however, it excited the fears of several English interests, and an agitation began, in favor of English interests, which lasted nearly forty years. It is a singular fact that Massachusetts interests were at first in harmony with the opponents of the petition. Cotton Mather wrote from London, May 19th, 1710, to Hon. John Saffin:—"The Virginia merchants think they shall get money by importing pig iron from Virginia, which consideration is so prevalent that they care not what distress they bring upon the poor inhabitants of the country. The principal thing they aim at is iron, notwithstanding they know that Parliament will not encourage the making that ore among us, without discouraging, at the same time, our manufactures. The Virginia merchants who petitioned Parliament for free importation of iron from the plantations, have done the same thing this session. Last time I had it flung out in the Lords; but I am now endeavoring to have iron left out of the bill, and in two votes I have been successful. I shall oppose it all I can, and be heard at the Lords' bar, if it goes up to them."

Three classes were interested discouraging importation of iron from America—the owners of forests, the makers of pig iron, and the manufacturers of iron wares. They said—the iron trade was never worse than now, and it will scarcely help it to reduce our furnaces and woods still further by importing more pig iron. If the importation of bar iron is encouraged, the steady market for it will enrich the makers so that they will go further and manufacture it: the charges for freight and handling would be too great to enable the colonies to send bar iron to England and take iron wares in return. Many forges in England are already dependent on American pig iron; and if more pig iron is imported, our woods would be cut for bar iron only, and their value lessened as less fuel would be needed, since pit-coal, instead of charcoal, could be used for the chafery fires. Then, too, said the *tanners*, if the value of wood is lessened, the coppices will be grubbed up, as they are almost profitless already, and we cannot procure *oak-bark* enough for our trade. We already pay four pounds sterling per ton for bark, and fear our business will be destroyed. All parties opposed to encouragement warned the committees that the importation of bar iron from America would not diminish that from Sweden nor save the money paid for Swedish bar. *American*

bar iron was like English—it did not equal Swedish iron—
and if encouraged would prevent the use of Swedish and
Russian irons *only after the destruction of the English
forges.* If the latter were destroyed, many thousand
families would come to ruin, for the iron trade employed
more hands "of the poor, laborious sort" than any other,
except the *woolen* trade, and certainly about 135,000 persons were maintained by it.

On the other hand, the owners of forges wished cheap
pig iron, the Bristol merchants desired trade, and the
manufacturers in general wished to increase exports of
woolen and other goods to America. These gentlemen
said the colonies already have furnaces and forges: it is
impossible to suppress them; but we can control them
to our own advantage. What law is more effectual than
interest? Encourage them to make pig and bar iron for
us by removing the duty on them, and then they can
take our goods. Otherwise they cannot pay us, even
for goods already sent. Warehouses were formerly kept
in the plantations to retail goods on the spot; but remittances are now so bad that the risk is too great for any
firm. The colonies will always buy goods of us, if they
can pay for them, since their labor is too dear to compete with ours in manufacture. As to the furnaces, we
ought not to raise the price of pig iron to help them, for
in that case we might help a few furnaces, but would
stop many forges. Our forges depend on American, or
at any rate on cheap, pig iron to compete with the soft
and cold-short Russian iron now selling so low. The
importation of American pig iron does not injure our
trade, for in 1731 we imported about as much as we now
do, yet our bar iron brought three pounds to three
pounds ten shillings sterling more than we get for it
now. Great Britain cannot make all the iron she needs;

for when iron was far higher than now, and our exports suffered from its dearness, we did not supply enough to reduce the price. Respecting our woods, opinions seem discordant—one party says make no bar iron, but send hither all your pig iron; another advises, make all your iron into bars in the colonies—send us no pig iron. We, too, believe the trade was never worse than at present; but the true causes of its decay are that we have no wars, hence no great demand for iron nor for the wood to make it; and that the owners of coppices have kept their price too high, and driven away trade when they could have secured it. The value of the woods depends on the price of iron. That is now twenty per cent. cheaper than it was some six years ago, so that forges must pay less for wood. Some of our forges are stopping now even with wood at seven shillings a cord, which they paid sixteen shillings for not long ago. If the English iron trade is lost, what would the woods be worth? The best way to help our iron trade is to aid our *nail trade*, which was never worse, and employs so few hands that the poor rates at Dudley are now (1738) twelve or thirteen pence in the pound instead of two or three pence, as they used to be. We need a vent for our works—a new market for our iron wares. We offer the clearest proof that the American iron equals Swedish both from the reports of Dockyard officers, who have used both kinds, and from the respective prices in the market. Hence, if we encourage the importation of American iron, we do not injure English forges, but relieve ourselves of a heavy debt to Sweden, and secure a growing market for our goods.

The question of encouragement was really decided by the proof of the fact that American iron was equal to Swedish, and better than the Russian and ordinary

English bar iron. The opponents of the measure stated that the American pig iron answered all the uses of British, and that the Birmingham makers reported that bars made of Baltimore iron equaled best English tough iron; but the greater part of the American iron was fit for nails only. The Baltimore iron was leaden tough, the Virginia cold-short, the Swedish both hard and tough. They denied that Baltimore and Virginia irons mixed would make an iron equal to Swedish. Other statements showed, however, that while Baltimore and Principio pig iron sold as cheap as English, yet it could not be denied that the bar iron made from them would, for many uses, answer as well as Swedish. It was proved conclusively by reports from all the Dock-yards, that American bar iron was equal in every respect to the best Swedish; that bar iron from the colonies, particularly from Philadelphia and Maryland, had " a strong body, and was very tough both hot and cold;" that Baltimore iron was better than two-thirds of the Swedish iron, and worth as much as the " second sort of Orgroon " (Dannemora) iron; and, finally, that the iron made in England from American pigs possessed the characteristics of American bars. As to price, it was shown that Swedish iron was sold in Bewdley at £14 per ton and £15 at London, and £15 to £17 for iron used for steel; that the best English tough sold for £16 at Bewdley; that the Russian (Moscow) bar iron sold for £11 per ton. On the other hand, the bar iron from Baltimore and Principio pigs sold at £16 to £16 1s. per ton; that New England bar iron cost £12 5s. to £12 10s. at a seaport, and could not be sold in England under £15 to £16. Further, with wood at 4 to 8 shil lings at the forge, there was no profit at Bewdley in £15 10s. for iron made from Maryland pigs, if the latter sold as high as £6 15s. Comparatively little iron was imported from Sweden for steel, as it was stated that only 900 to 1000 tons of steel were made in England about 1738; so the price of iron for steel could be no criterion.

The matter was finally determined, in 1749, rather in accordance with the views of the merchants who traded with the colonies. Pig iron was allowed to be imported free to all parts of the kingdom, so as to secure cheap bar iron. But bar iron could not be imported at any port but London, and carried no further than ten miles from that city. This clause was intended to aid the owners of woods. In order to protect the nail trade, all slitting-mills in the colonies were ordered to be destroyed. The following act of Parliament, expressing the above policy, was passed in 1749 (twenty-third year George II.), remaining in force till the Revolution. A copy of it is preserved by the Historical Society of Pennsylvania :—

AN ACT

To encourage the Importation of Pig and Bar Iron from His Majesty's Colonies in America; and to prevent the Erection of any Mill or other Engine for Slitting or Rolling of Iron; or any Plateing Forge to work with a Tilt Hammer, or any Furnace for making Steel in any of the said Colonies.

WHEREAS, The Importation of Bar Iron from His Majesty's Colonies in America into the Port of London, and the Importation of Pig Iron from the said Colonies, into any Port of Great Britain, and the Manufacture of such Bar and Pig Iron in Great Britain, will be a great Advantage, not only to the said Colonies, but also to this Kingdom, by furnishing the Manufacturers of Iron with a supply of that useful and necessary Commodity, and by means thereof large sums of Money, now annually paid for Iron to Foreigners, will be saved to this Kingdom, and a greater quantity of the Woollen, and other Manufactures of Great Britain, will be exported to America in Exchange for such Iron so imported; be it therefore enacted by the King's Most Excellent Majesty, by and with the advice and consent of the Lords, Spiritual and Temporal, and Commons, in this present Parliament assembled, and by the authority of the same, That from and after the Twenty-fourth day of June, one thousand seven hundred and fifty, the several and respective Subsidies, Customs, Impositions, Rates, and Duties now payable on Pig Iron, made in and imported from His Majesty's Colonies in America, into any Port of Great Britain, shall cease, determine, and be no longer paid; and that from and after the said Twenty-fourth day of June, no Subsidy, Custom, Imposition, Rate, or Duty whatever, shall be payable upon Bar Iron made in and imported from the said Colonies, into the Port of London; any Law, Statute, or usage to the contrary thereof in any wise notwithstanding.

And be it further enacted by the Authority aforesaid, That no such Bar Iron so imported into the Port of London shall be afterwards exported, or shall be carried Coastwise to be landed at any other Port or Place of Great Britain, except for the use of His Majesty's Dock Yards, upon Pain, that all such Bar Iron so exported, or carried Coastwise, and every Ship or Vessel, on Board of which any such Bar Iron shall be so exported, or carried Coastwise, shall be subject to such forfeiture and seizure, as any prohibited or uncustomed Goods, or any Goods clandestinely exported or imported, or any Ship or Vessel, on Board of which any such Goods shall be exported or imported, are now liable by Law; and also upon Pain, that every Person so exporting such Bar Iron, or sending the same Coastwise, and the Master or Commander and Mariners of every Ship or Vessel, on Board of which any such Bar Iron shall be so exported or carried Coastwise, shall be subject to such and the like Punishments and Penalties as the Master or Commander, or Mariners of any Ship or Vessel, laden with any prohibited or uncustomed Goods, or Goods clandestinely exported or imported, are now liable to by Law; and that no Officer of His Majesty's Customs shall sign or grant any Cocquet, Sufferance, Transire, Let-pass, Warrant, or Certificate whatsoever, for exporting or carrying Coastwise, except for the use of His Majesty's Dock Yards, any such Bar Iron so imported into the Port of London, upon Pain, that every Officer of His Majesty's Customs, so offending, shall forfeit and pay the Sum of Two Hundred Pounds, to be sued for and recovered by Action, Bill, Plaint, or Information, in any of His Majesty's Courts of Record at Westminster, and to be applied, one Moiety to the use of His Majesty, his Heirs and Successors, and the other Moiety to such Person or Persons as shall sue for the same, and shall also lose and forfeit his Office, and be incapable of serving His Majesty, his Heirs or Successors, in any Office of Trust or Profit whatsoever; and that if any such Cocquet, Sufferance, Transire, Let-pass, Warrant, or Certificate whatsoever shall be signed or granted, the same shall be void, and of no Effect whatsoever.

And be it further enacted by the Authority aforesaid, That no Bar Iron whatsoever shall be permitted to be carried Coastwise, unless mention be made in the Certificate to be granted for that Purpose, of the Day on which the Subsidies, Customs, Impositions, Rates, and Duties, payable upon the Importation thereof, were paid, and of the Name of the Person or Persons by whom the same were paid.

And it is hereby further enacted, That no Bar Iron imported into the Port of London, by virtue or in pursuance of this Act, shall be carried or conveyed by Land Carriage to any Place beyond Ten Miles from any Part of the Port of London, except to His Majesty's Dock Yards for the use of His Majesty, his Heirs and Successors; and if any Person or Persons shall carry and convey, or cause or procure to be carried or conveyed upon Horseback, or in any Waggon, Cart, or other Carriage, any Iron so imported, to any Place beyond the limits prescribed by this Act, every Person so offending shall, for every such offence, forfeit and pay the Sum of Twenty Shillings for every hundredweight of such Iron.

And that the Importers of Foreign Pig and Bar Iron, not made in and imported from the said Colonies, may not, upon any Pretence whatsoever, claim the Exemption hereby granted; be it further enacted by the Authority aforesaid, That every Merchant, Trader, Factor, or other Person, loading any Pig or Bar Iron on Board any Ship or Vessel in any of His Majesty's Colonies in America, shall, before the clearing out of the said Ship or Vessel for any Port of Great Britain, make Oath before the Governor or Lieutenant Governor, Collector and Comptroller of the Customs, and Naval Officer, or any Two of them (which Oath every such Governor or Lieutenant Governor, Collector and Comptroller of the Customs, and Naval Officer is hereby impowered and required to administer without Fee or Reward) that the Pig or Bar Iron so shipped, the true Weight whereof shall in such Oath be expressed, was made at —— within the Colony of —— in which Oath also the Name or Names of the Person or Persons to whom the said Iron shall be sold or consigned, shall be expressed; and thereupon the said Governor, Lieutenant Governor, Collector and Comptroller of the Customs, and Naval Officer, or any Two of them shall deliver to such Merchant, Trader, Factor, or other Person, so making Oath as aforesaid, a Certificate, under their Hands and Seal of Office, of such Oath having been made before them.

And be it further enacted by the Authority aforesaid, That no Person or Persons importing any Pig or Bar Iron into Great Britain from His Majesty's Colonies in America, shall import the same Duty-free as aforesaid, unless such Pig or Bar Iron shall be stamped with some Mark denoting the Colony or Place where the same was made; and unless such Person or Persons shall produce such Certificate to the Chief Officer of the Customs at the Port in Great Britain where the same shall be imported; and unless Oath shall be made before the said Chief Officer of the Customs, by the Master or Commanding Officer of the Ship or Vessel importing such Pig or Bar Iron (which Oath such Chief Officer is hereby impowered and required to administer without Fee or Reward) that the Iron so imported is the same Iron mentioned in the said Certificate.

Provided always, and be it enacted by the Authority aforesaid, That all Pig or Bar Iron imported into Great Britain, which shall not be so stamped and certified as aforesaid, to be made in His Majesty's Colonies in America, shall be subject to the Payment of the same Subsidies, Customs, Importations, Rates, and Duties to which such Iron was liable before the making of this Act.

And be it further enacted by the Authority aforesaid, That if any Governor, Lieutenant Governor, Collector or Comptroller of the Customs, Naval Officer, or Chief Officer of the Customs as aforesaid, shall falsely make any such Certificate, every Person so offending shall, for every such Offence, forfeit and pay the Sum of Two Hundred Pounds, and also forfeit and lose his Office, and be incapable of serving His Majesty, his Heirs and Successors, in any Office of Trust or Profit; or if any Merchant, Factor, Trader, and Master, or Commanding Officer of any Ship or Vessel, shall falsely make any Oath required by this Act, every such Offender shall incur the Punishment inflicted by the Laws of this Realm for willful and corrupt Perjury; and if any Person shall knowingly counterfeit any such Stamp, or shall counterfeit any such Certificate, or publish the same, knowing it to be Counterfeit, every such Person so offending shall incur the Punishment inflicted by the Laws of this Realm for Forgery.

And, that Pig and Bar Iron made in His Majesty's Colonies in America may be further manufactured in this Kingdom, be it further enacted by the Authority aforesaid, That from and after the Twenty-fourth day of June, one thousand seven hundred and fifty, no Mill or other Engine for Slitting or Rolling of Iron, or any Plateing Forge to work with a Tilt Hammer, or any Furnace for making Steel shall be erected, or after such Erection continued in any of His Majesty's Colonies in America; and if any Person or Persons shall erect, or cause to be erected, or after such Erection, continue, or cause to be continued, in any of the said Colonies, any such Mill, Engine, Forge, or Furnace, every Person or Persons so offending shall, for every such Mill, Engine, Forge, or Furnace forfeit the Sum of Two Hundred Pounds of lawful Money of Great Britain.

And it is hereby further enacted by the Authority aforesaid, That every such Mill, Engine, Forge, or Furnace, so erected or continued, contrary to

the Directions of this Act, shall be deemed a COMMON NUISANCE, and that
every Governor, Lieutenant Governor, or Commander-in-Chief of any of
His Majesty's Colonies in America, where any such Mill, Engine, Forge, or
Furnace shall be erected or continued, shall, upon Information to him made
and given, upon the Oath of any Two or more Credible Witnesses, that any
such Mill, Engine, Forge, or Furnace hath been so erected or continued
(which Oath such Governor, Lieutenant Governor, or Commander-in-Chief
is hereby authorized and required to administer) order and cause every
such Mill, Engine, Forge, or Furnace to be abated within the Space of Thirty
Days next after such Information given and made as aforesaid; and if any
Governor, Lieutenant Governor, or Commander-in-Chief, shall neglect or
refuse so to do, within the Time hereinbefore limited for that purpose, every
such Governor, Lieutenant Governor, or Commander-in-Chief, so offending, shall, for every such offence, forfeit the sum of Five Hundred Pounds
of lawful Money of Great Britain, and shall from thenceforth be disabled
to hold or enjoy any Office of Trust or Profit under His Majesty, his Heirs,
or Successors.

And it is hereby further enacted by the Authority aforesaid, That the
several Penalties and Forfeitures by this Act inflicted for falsely making
any Stamp or Certificate, hereinbefore directed, or for erecting or con-
tinuing any Mill, Engine, Plateing Forge, or Furnace, prohibited by this
Act, or for refusing or neglecting to abate the same, shall and may be
sued for and recovered by Action, Bill, Plaint, or Information, in any of
His Majesty's Courts of Record at Westminster, or in the Court of Ex-
chequer in Scotland, or in any of the Courts of Record in His Majesty's
Colonies in America respectively, wherein the Offender shall dwell at the
Time when the Offence shall be committed, or at the Time when such Action,
Bill, Plaint, or Information shall be brought; and every such Action, Bill,
Plaint, or Information, to be brought in Great Britain, shall be laid either
in the County where any such Offence shall be committed, or where the
Offender shall dwell at the Time when such Action, Bill, Plaint, or Infor-
mation shall be brought.

And be it further enacted by the Authority aforesaid, That all such
Penalties and Forfeitures shall be applied, one Moiety to the use of His
Majesty, his Heirs, and Successors, and the other Moiety to such Person or
Persons as shall sue for the same.

And it is hereby further enacted by the Authority aforesaid, That all
Bar Iron which shall be imported from any of His Majesty's Colonies in
America into the Port of London, by virtue or under the Authority of this
present Act, shall be entered at the Custom House in London; and every
Bar of the said Iron so entered, shall be marked or stamped with such Mark

or Stamp as the Commissioners of His Majesty's Customs shall for that Purpose order or direct, in Three different Parts of every such Bar, (that is to say) Two of said Marks or Stamps at the distance of One Yard from each End of such Bar, and the other of them at or near the Middle thereof.

And it is hereby further enacted, That if any Person shall counterfeit, or willfully destroy or deface, any of the said Marks or Stamps, with an Intent to convey or carry the same to any Place Ten Miles from any Part of the Port of London, contrary to the true Meaning of this Act, every Person so offending, and being thereof legally convicted, shall forfeit the Sum of One Hundred Pounds, to be recovered by Action of Debt, Bill, Plaint, or Information, in any of His Majesty's Courts of Record at Westminster; one Moiety thereof to His Majesty, his Heirs, and Successors, and the other Moiety to such Person or Persons who shall sue for the same.

And be it further enacted by the Authority aforesaid, That from and after the said Twenty-fourth Day of June, every Governor, or Lieutenant Governor, or Commander-in-Chief, of any of His Majesty's Colonies in America, shall forthwith transmit to the Commissioners for Trade and Plantations, a Certificate under his Hand and Seal of Office, containing a particular Account of every Mill or Engine for Slitting and Rolling Iron; and every Plateing Forge to work with a Tilt Hammer; and every Furnace for making Steel, at the Time of the Commencement of this Act, erected in his Colony; expressing also in the said Certificate such of them as are used, and the Name or Names of the Proprietor or Proprietors of each such Mill, Engine, Forge, and Furnace, and the Place where each such Mill, Engine, Forge, and Furnace is erected, and the number of Engines, Forges, and Furnaces in the said Colony; and if any Governor, Lieutenant Governor, or Commander-in-Chief, shall neglect or refuse so to do within Six Months after the said Twenty-fourth Day of June, every such Governor, Lieutenant Governor, or Commander-in-Chief so offending, shall be subject to such Penalties and Forfeitures, as any Governor or Lieutenant Governor of any of the said Colonies is liable to for any Offence committed against this Act, to be recovered in like Manner as is by this Act directed for the same.

And be it further enacted by the Authority aforesaid, That if any Action or Suit shall be commenced against any Person or Persons for anything done in pursuance of this Act, the Defendant or Defendants in any such Action or Suit may plead the General Issue, and give this Act and the Special Matter in Evidence, at any Trial to be had thereupon; and that the same was done in pursuance and by the Authority of this Act; and if it shall appear to have been done, the Jury shall find for the Defendant or Defendants; and if the Plaintiff shall be nonsuited, or discontinue his

Action after the Defendant or Defendants shall have appeared, or if Judge-
ment shall be given upon a Verdict or Demurrer against the Plaintiff, the
Defendant or Defendants shall and may recover Treble Costs, and have the
like Remedy for the same, as any Defendant or Defendants hath or have in
other Cases by Law.

And be it further enacted by the Authority aforesaid, That this Act shall
be deemed a Public Act, and be judicially taken Notice of as such, by all
Judges, Justices, and other Persons whatsoever, without specially pleading
the same.

In 1756 this act was modified so as to permit the free
importation of American iron into all the ports of Great
Britain; and in 1765 another was passed, allowing the
shipment of iron from the colonies to Ireland, and its
importation duty free.

In accordance with the act of 23 George II. (1749),
the governors of all the American colonies returned the
number of rolling or slitting mills, plating-forges, with
tilt-hammers and steel-works in their district. Massachusetts Bay had two slitting-mills, one plating-forge,
and one steel-furnace; Connecticut, six plating-forges
and one steel-furnace; New York, one plating-forge,
not in use, and one steel furnace; Maryland, one plating-
forge, with two tilt-hammers; New Jersey, one slitting-
mill, *reported* not in use; Pennsylvania, one slitting-mill,
one plating-forge, and two steel-furnaces. All these
works were, of course, suppressed till the colonies
declared their independence. This arbitrary act gave
great offence in the colonies. Even the colonial officers
who had given information concerning the industries of
their districts did not escape animadversion, and Surveyor-general Dunbar, of Massachusetts, was mobbed.

We thus see that, notwithstanding all obstacles, the
American colonies could make pig iron more cheaply
than the English works, and sell it in England at a

profit; but that, by legislation, they were restricted to making pig iron to exchange for English wares. The Revolution destroyed this condition of things and gave great impetus to the American manufacture between 1775 and 1783. Prices rose exceedingly, on account of the demand for iron and the depreciation of the currency. Mrs. James, in her "Potts' Memorial," collected the prices paid at Colebrookdale, during a series of years, in Pennsylvania currency ($2.66=£1).

	£	s.	
In 1731 pig iron at Colebrookdale furnace brought	5	0	per ton.
In 1765 pig iron at Colebrookdale furnace brought	7	0	" "
In 1767 pig iron at Colebrookdale furnace brought	8	10	" "
In 1774–1776 pig iron at Colebrookdale furnace brought	7 · 5		" "
In 1781 pig iron at Colebrookdale furnace brought, in hard money, . .	10	0	" "
In 1784 pig iron at Colebrookdale furnace brought, in hard money, . .	11	10	" "
In 1762 bar iron brought . . .	34	0	" "
In 1781 bar iron for slitting brought, in hard money, ...	35	0	" "

In 1778 Robert Levers wrote to the Board of War, at Philadelphia, that two tons of iron at the Chelsea forge could be sold at £200 per ton, and in 1779, on receipt of orders to sell, found he could get £300 per ton for it from the smiths of the neighborhood. He remarked that £1000, in 1779, was no more than £80 some years before, and that a house rented for £13 in 1778 brought £100 in 1779. This state of things in Pennsylvania and New Jersey was not exceptional, but one equally felt in all the colonies, through the unlimited issue of paper money.

Laborers were so scarce in 1776 that all men at iron-works were exempted from military duty, and works in the counties of Lancaster, Chester, and Berks, in Pennsylvania, employed in casting cannon and shot, were allowed to employ prisoners of war.

After the Revolution no trade regulations were made by the colonies till 1790,—importation being entirely free and internal taxes heavy. Meanwhile England had the advantage of Onion's and Cort's inventions of puddling (1783) and of Cort's grooved rolls (1784). Abraham Darby had succeeded, in 1735, at Colebrookdale, in using coke in the blast-furnace. Before the Revolution there were many coke and raw-coal furnaces at work in England, and by 1796 charcoal-furnaces had been praccally abandoned. Smeaton had constructed cast-iron blowing cylinders at Carrow, in 1760, and Wilkinson, not long afterwards, operated them by Watt's steam-engine, and the double-acting blowing-engine was designed in 1769. On the other hand, American machinery was then poor, transportation difficult and very expensive, soft coal out of the way in the wilderness, and anthracite unknown as a fuel for iron manufacture. Great Britain, therefore, held the American market and ruined American works. We could not then imitate English work for want of capital, engineering skill, and coal, and the copying of machinery was made as difficult as possible by act of Parliament, 1785, thus:—It was forbidden to export any tools, engines, models, or plans of machines used for making iron, under a penalty of a year's imprisonment, £200 fine, and confiscation of the articles shipped or *intended* to be shipped; £200 fine upon the master of the vessel; and upon any custom-house officer offending there was added dismissal and incapacity to hold office. A year's imprisonment and £500 fine was the penalty for enticing a workman, doubled on the second offense.

Besides her successful efforts to secure markets for her iron wares and manufactured goods, England adopted a prohibitive course in laying duties on imported iron, and absolutely forbade the admission of hammered or slit bars under three-quarters of an inch square. This policy was maintained uninterruptedly for one hundred and forty-seven years; that is, until internal competition, under prohibitive duties and the improvements of manufacture had so diminished prices that England controlled the markets of the world. If history has any weight, or the force of example any value, the success of England under this policy should induce every nation to follow her example. A century and a half is too long a period for an *experiment*, and when, by a persistent policy, a country has been raised to the highest pinnacle of prosperity, it is too late to say that the methods employed have been *failures*, or the measures ill advised.

DUTY ON BAR IRON IMPORTED IN ENGLISH SHIPS INTO GREAT BRITAIN.

		£	s.	d.
In 1679 a duty was laid of	. . .	0	10	0
In 1710 " "	. . .	2	1	6
In 1782 " "	. . .	2	16	2
In 1796 " "	. . .	3	1	9
In 1797 " "	. . .	3	4	7
In 1798 " "	. . .	3	15	5
In 1803 " "	. . .	4	4	4½

	£	s.	d.
In 1804 a duty was laid of . . .	4	17	1
In 1805 " " . . .	5	1	0
In 1806 " " . . .	5	7	5¾
In 1809 " " . . .	5	9	10
In 1813 " " . . .	6	9	10
In 1819 " " . . .	6	10	0

In 1825 English bars were worth (Villefosse) ten pounds sterling at Cardiff, while Russian and Swedish could not be sold under thirteen pounds thirteen shillings sterling. The exports of iron exceeded ninety thousand tons, and were increasing vastly, so that its object having been accomplished the duty was reduced to one pound ten shillings sterling.

Having thus traced the history of the iron manufacture in all the colonies up to the Revolution, we shall devote our attention to Pennsylvania alone. In the following details we present, under the names of the respective counties, all the information that is accessible concerning her iron trade until the present time.

ADAMS COUNTY, formed in 1800 out of York county. A belt of limestone crosses the south-east corner, rising under the secondary red shales and red sandstone, which form the greater part of the county. The sandstone is broken in places by dykes of trap-rocks, associated in many instances with thin veins of magnetic iron-ore. To the west the South mountains, a group of high, narrow, anticlinal ridges of primal rocks, contain brown hematite ore, mainly in the valleys to the west of the county line.

Though Thaddeus Stevens' Graeffenburg estate lies in this county, the Caledonia furnace itself lies in Franklin county. The only iron made in Adams county was made by Stevens & Paxton, at the Maria furnace, built about 1843, and long since abandoned.

ALLEGHENY COUNTY, formed in 1788 out of parts of Westmoreland and Washington counties. It lies in the great western or Fifth coal basin of Pennsylvania. The Pittsburg bed of coal is five and one-half feet to ten feet thick and yields the purest coal. This great bed is finely exposed at Pittsburg and along nearly the whole length of the Monongahela river, covering an area of not less than 14,000 square miles. There are no clay iron-stones here associated with it, hence the iron-ores used in the county must be brought thither. Above the coal, however, a massive belt of limestone provides ample material for flux.

Coal was known before 1765, but not mined till 1784, about twenty years after the town lots of Pittsburg had been laid out. The Penns granted privileges to mine coal in the hill opposite the city, or Coal Hill, "to dig coal as far in as the perpendicular line falling from the summit of the hill," a charge of £30 sterling per lot. The Monongahela collieries were first opened about twenty-eight years ago.

In 1790 the first furnace was built on the Youghiogheny, and another soon after near Pittsburg. The latter was located at the present Shadyside station of the Pennsylvania Railroad, or about the geographical centre of Pittsburg. It was built between 1790 and 1792, by George Anshutz, who then managed the Westmoreland furnace, three miles from Fort Ligonier, and afterwards built or became part owner of the Huntingdon furnace. The product was mainly hollow ware, and the furnace was very soon abandoned for want of ore. Mr. Anshutz came to this country in 1789, from Strasburg, on the Rhine, where he had conducted a foundry business. The first rolling-mill (Pittsburg Rolling-mill) was built in 1812, at Pittsburg, by C. Cowan. In 1818–20 bar iron sold at Pittsburg for $190 to $200, boiler iron $350, hoop iron $250 per ton, and sheet iron $18 per cwt. English vises were worth there 20 to 22½ cents per pound! The engine at the Union mill cost $11,000 in 1819, and a much better one, of 130 horse-power, for the Sligo mill, cost, in 1826, only $3000.

Splendid coal and an unrivaled geographical position have made Pittsburg the greatest iron-manufacturing locality in the country. About 1835, when the great centre of iron production lay in Huntingdon and Centre counties, the blooms made in that region were sent to Pittsburg and the coal-fields, instead of being rolled on the spot, with coal carried thither. Up to about the year 1840 the Pittsburg mills thus depended mainly on transported blooms, and though the city had long had so many rolling-mills, it made no pig iron before 1856, and is still the most important market for pig iron in the country.

In 1826 there were 6 rolling-mills in Pittsburg,—the Sligo, built in 1825, by R. T. Stewart & I. Lyon, to use Juniata blooms, as did also the Juniata Works, built in 1824 by Dr. Shoenberger. The other mills were the Pittsburg, Grant's Hill, Union, and Dowlais; the total product was said to reach 4600 tons a year; but *Hazard's Register* gives the total product of the same works, in 1831, at 1631 tons. The Iron Committee, of the Friends of Home Industry, stated that in 1831 there were "eight rolling and slitting" mills in Pittsburg, and members of the committee resident in Pittsburg vouched for the following figures, which are greatly overestimated if Harris and Hazard are to be believed :—

in 1828, 3291 tons 19 cwt.; in 1829, 6217 tons 17 cwt.; in 1830, 9282 tons 2 cwt.

In 1840 there were in the county 28 charcoal-furnaces, producing 6584 tons of pig iron, and 12 "bloomeries and forges" (including rolling-mills), the product of which was 28,100 tons of bar iron.

In 1850 Allegheny county contained fourteen rolling-mills, all of which lay in Pittsburg. A summary of their operations, made from the tables of Charles E. Smith, results as follows:—

Number of puddling-furnaces, ...	129
Number of heating-furnaces, ...	88
Number of roll-trains, ...	54
Number of nail-machines, ...	246
Consumption of coal, . .	3,932,000 bushels.
Consumption of wood, ...	900 cords.
Consumption of pig iron, ...	50,360 tons.
Consumption of blooms, ...	8,880 tons.
Consumption of scrap, ...	3,100 tons.
Product (largest) of wrought iron, . .	49,932 tons.
Product (actual) in 1849, wrought iron, .	43,220 tons.

There were also 2 steel-works in operation (Singer, Hartman & Co., 1848; Pittsburg Steel-works, 1835), with a total product of 1900 tons of steel; and there were or had been 4 other steel-works (Coleman, Hailman & Co., Spang & Co., G. & J. H. Shoenberger, S. McKelvy), of which the estimated capacity was 1378 tons yearly, but nothing further is recorded of them. At this date the steel manufacture was mainly confined to converted steel, and it is quite probable that the amount of cast steel made did not reach 500 tons.

In 1856 there were rolling-mills, but no furnaces or forges, at work in the county. The product of the mills, 19 of which, with 408 furnaces in all, were in Pittsburg, was estimated at the following amounts:—

CONSUMPTION.

105,333 tons pig iron, ...	$3,159,990 00
27,267 tons blooms, ...	2,181,360 00
4,931 tons scrap iron, . . .	186,440 00
2,550 tons Swedes and rolled iron, .	178,500 60
6 187,515 bushels coal, ...	251,500 60
118,000 bushels coke, ...	5,900 00
5,040 tons fire-clay, ...	21,500 00
2,095,000 tons fire-brick, . . .	41,900 00
9,258 tons ore, ...	120,696 00
51,800 gallons oil and grease, . .	53,034 00
Small items to amount to .	43,000 00
	$6,243,821 20

PRODUCT.

3,212½ tons boiler iron, . . .	$388,712 00
67,100 tons bar iron, ...	4,697,000 00
5,637 tons sheet iron, . . .	681,077 00
699,762 kegs nails, spikes, rivets, . .	2,797,048 00
10,000 boxes tacks, ...	50,000 00
800 tons galvanized and imitation Russia iron, ...	96,000 00
10,850 tons blister-plow, spring, and cast steel, ...	1,747,850 00
2,500 crowbars, ...	5,000 00
1,800 sledges, ...	1,875 00
Axles to amount of	80,500 00
Springs to amount of	135,000 00
Vises, ...	50,000 00
	$10,730,062 00

In 1873 there were in the county 11 coke-furnaces, with a product of 163,836 tons of pig iron; 29 rolling-mills, which made 251,161 tons of iron; 2 rail-mills, with a product of 22,856 tons; 9 cast-steel works, which made 25,822 tons, and 1 Bessemer-steel works—the Edgar Thomson—in the course of erection, since completed and started August 26th, 1875.

In 1875 the city of Pittsburg alone contained 31 rolling-mills, with the following "plant":—

Number of puddling-furnaces, including 6 Dank's rotary furnaces, ... 754
Number of heating-furnaces, ... 268
Number of trains of rolls, ... 173
Number of hammers, ... 30
Number of nail and spike machines, . . . 452
Number of tack-machines, ... 50
Capacity in net tons at least 405,000 tons.

There were 12 steel-works, besides 2 iron-works which also made steel, and the steel-making plant consisted of the following parts:—

Number of open-hearth steel-melting furnaces, . 6
Number of Siemen's 24-pot melting-furnaces, . 24
Number of cementing-furnaces, ... 34
Number of melting-holes, ... 324
Number of puddling-furnaces, ... 35
Number of heating-furnaces, ... 125
Number of trains of rolls, ... 35
Number of hammers, ... 72
Capacity in net tons at least 47,000 tons.

The products given above for 1873 are those on which comparisons with statements of earlier periods should properly be based, since production has been quite irregular, as to locality, since the panic which occurred in the fall of 1873. We have, therefore, prepared to make 1873 the concluding epoch of our comparisons throughout this work. An illustration of our meaning appears in the statistics of the production of Pittsburg and Allegheny county for 1874 and 1875; the quantities are in net tons.

Product of Iron and Steel—Allegheny County.

Year.	Kind of Works.	Number.	Pig Iron.	Rails, Bar, Angle, Bolt, Rod, and Hoop.	Sheet and Plate.	Nails, Kegs.	Total weight Iron.	Crucible Steel.	Blister, German and Open-hearth Steel.	Total Steel.
1874	Blast-furnace.	11	143,660	....	....	....	....	....	....	....
1875	Blast-furnace.	11	131,856	....	....	....	....	....	....	....
1874	Rolling-mill.	31	....	194,114	52,361	562,995	274,625	....	....	....
1875	Rolling-mill.	32	....	177,733	45,773	442,359	245,624	....	....	....
1874	* Steel-works.	10	....	....	....	....	....	17,915	6,000	28,915
1875	* Steel-works.	13	....	....	....	....	....	22,942	6,860	25,802

* This does not include Bessemer steel-works; four of these steel-works are also in rolling-mills.

Two works had beeñ exclusively occupied in producing steel castings of crucible steel, by methods like that followed at Naylor, Vickers & Co.'s, Sheffield, or at Bochum. It is gratifying to see that all obstacles have been overcome (inexperience, untried moulding-sand mixtures, quality and grade of steel, &c.), and that within a year from the building of the first works a second has been put into operation.

No remarks can increase the impressiveness of the statistics quoted above. It is enough to say that the city which made, in 1831, only sixteen hundred and thirty-one tons of iron, now produces fully one-sixth of all the wrought iron made in the United States. The following cut of Pittsburg in 1842 will show, better than words, how this increase has been brought about. The mill in the foreground is the Eagle Rolling-mill as it then existed :—

VIEW OF PITTSBURG (1842), FROM THE MOUTH OF SAW-MILL RUN, ON THE OHIO.

The Sligo mill, on the south side of the Mononga-hela, got its coal from an adjoining mine, and was the first mill west of the Alleghenies to introduce the Bur-den squeezer. The Wayne Iron-works was the next to use Burden's squeezer; and during the time of Brown, Miltenberger & Co., or about 1841, "the Bessemer pro-cess is said to have been tried in the mill," I suppose as an application of the refinery, pretty much as Parry tried his experiment at Ebbwvale. The Juniata and other works used the refinery, but since 1864, or about that date, all our mills have boiled grey forge iron in prefer-ence to puddling refined iron. A technical description of the present Pittsburg mills would be highly interest-ing, but would far exceed our limits. A school of roll-ing-mill engineering is being there developed, which, like the English, has the object of doing good work as cheaply as possible. Everything seems made for use, and the designs now applied are modern and characteristic. There is no doubt whatever but that this trait proves a profitable one commercially, and that Pittsburg industries are seldom hampered by capital unduly laid out in buildings or idle parts of a plant. An interesting feature is the great diversity of product. One finds mills in Pittsburg which produce nearly all kinds of iron and steel almost under one roof.

The Sligo, Juniata, and other works had won the highest reputations .on products from their own furnaces and forges in Clarion, Centre, and Huntingdon counties. The suggestion that the other works should make their own pig iron was often considered, but for the want of ore at convenient distances little was done till the Pittsburg trade was planted in the civil war on an impregnable basis, and organized transportation made the ores of Lake Superior accessible. The Clinton furnace (1859), the two Eliza furnaces (1861), and the two Superior furnaces (1862–3) were all forty-five feet high and twelve feet diameter at the boshes, dimensions which were long the favorite ones, owing to ill success of the 15-foot furnaces first erected. The product of the Clinton furnace is a high one, notwithstanding its size, for it made 11,082 gross tons in 1874. The two Shoenberger stacks, 47 by 13 feet, use a large portion of Canada magnetic ore, and made in 1874 15,273 tons of 2268 pounds each.

About 1872 a change—an enlargement of dimensions and power, utilizing English ideas—took place in blast furnace construction which has placed Pittsburg at the head of the trade as respects blast furnace product. The Lucy furnace (75 feet high, 20 feet bosh), the two

Isabella furnaces (No. 1, 75 feet and 18 feet, and No. 2, 75 feet and 20 feet), and the Soho furnace (65 feet and 19 feet) were all blown in about the same time, in 1872. They all have the iron-jacketed stack, resting on iron columns, bolted to a circular foundation plate, now universally used, and first built in this country by Ralph Crooker at Port Henry.

The Isabella furnaces were built by Mr. Benjamin Crowther, and each has independent air hoists, stoves, blast mains, &c. In an engine house 111 feet long, 40 feet wide, and 40½ feet high, stand 5 short-stroke blowing engines, with balanced slide valves, by Mackintosh, Hemphill & Co.; their exhaust passes into four Stillwell heaters placed behind them. The stroke is 4 feet, and the diameter of the blowing cylinders is 84 inches and of the steam cylinders 34 inches. Blast pipes 4 feet in diameter, and each 375 feet long to the stoves, act as reservoirs to equalize pressure. Adjoining the engine-house, but at right angles to it, the boiler-house—79 feet wide, 85 feet long, and 35 feet high—contains 12 cylinder boilers 64 feet long and 42 inches in diameter, fed by 2 Cameron pumps. Gas is conducted to the boilers through a subterranean flue 4½ feet wide and 6 feet deep and 260 feet in length. Immediately in rear of the furnaces stand 10 hot-blast stoves, with pipes 4 by 16 inches in the two diameters, corrugated inside, and 14 feet long. The blast is heated to 1000°, and each furnace is blown through 7 tuyeres, 6½ inches in diameter, with a blast at not less than 7 pounds to the square inch. Adjoining the stoves to the rear is the stock-house, 240 feet long, 75 feet wide, and 34 feet high, in which 10,000 tons of Lake Superior ore can be stored, and the coke, from the company's own works at Blairsville, is dumped into hopper bins, from which it falls into the barrows. The Lucy is equally well built, and has used one of Mr. Kloman's slag-cooling turntables, which carries a series of slag-cooling cast-iron boxes around in an annular water-trough. An eye-bar is placed upright in each box, the slag cools round it and is lifted out by means of it on coming under a crane.

The Lucy furnace has been making mainly Bessemer iron of a high grade, while the Isabella furnaces have produced mainly forge iron of the utmost uniformity. In regard to product these works have been running a friendly race, in the course of which they have attracted more attention than any other furnaces in the country. The No. 2 Isabella, as first lined, made 350 to 470 tons a week, with 27 to 28 hundredweight of coke to the ton. In 1875 its shape was altered; its capacity reduced several thousand cubic feet to 12,000 cubic feet, and with the same ores, fuels, and flux as before, it is now making over 700 tons per week; the greatest yield was $770\frac{660}{2240}$ tons; and in 16 weeks, from September 25th, 1875, to January 15th, 1876, 11,329 gross tons were made. The No. 1 produced in 1875 a weekly average of $640\frac{1769}{2240}$ tons of pig iron. This great increase of product is ascribed to the change of shape and to the great quantity of blast, which is forced in at a pressure of 8 to 9 pounds per square inch. The Lucy furnace made in 4 weeks, ending September 18th, 1875, this date ending the seventh week of a new blast, $2395\frac{1520}{2240}$, almost entirely Bessemer Nos. 1 and 2, and in one week (the fifth) made $606\frac{432}{2240}$ tons. In the last three weeks of October, 1875, the furnace made respectively 680.1, 762, and 707.02 tons, of 2268 pounds each, with 3348 to 3434 pounds of coke, counting five per cent. waste.

Art has improved the rich opportunity of nature's gifts to this region. The Allegheny, Monongahela, and Ohio furnish the cheapest roads running along the out-crop of the coal-seams, and the slackwater navigation of the Monongahela makes the road capable of transporting yearly more than 2,500,000 tons of coal. The introduction of coal-washing machinery has enabled manufacturers to run their works on slack and ship the lump coal away if desired. Not content with her favors, nature has placed at disposal, so long as it may last, the natural gas of the oil districts to save the labor of mining. A novel danger assails the region—a superfluity of natural advantages and the heedless waste incident to plenty; but the improvements in furnaces, mill-work, and general practice recently made show that Pittsburg has happily passed the period of danger on that score.

Messrs. Rogers & Burchfield were the first to use natural gas for iron-working in their puddling furnaces at Leechburg, Armstrong county. Their well, 3 inches in diameter, was sunk in 1871, on the left bank of the Kiskiminetas, for oil, to a depth of 1250 feet; nothing but gas and a little salt water having been obtained, it was abandoned. It was bought by Rogers & Burchfield in 1874, and the gas conveyed, at a pressure of 70 pounds, to their works, on the right bank of the creek, by a 5-inch pipe, with which all their fires were connected. The pipe bridge across the creek having been carried away by a freshet, it was found a 3-inch pipe would do the work. In using the gas in the ordinary puddling furnace the only change made was to brick up the bridge of the furnaces and let the gas in through iron pipes, supplying air by a blast. Blast pipes were also inserted in the crown of the furnace in such a way that the blast should strike the metal at an angle of 90°, blast being let on at the commencement of the boil. By this means iron could be made, from ordinary coke gray forge pig, equal in quality to that made from the best charcoal iron, and at a cost, as was claimed, of $50 per ton less, and without the use of the "knobbling fire."

The most remarkable gas-wells, however, have so far been bored in Parker township, of Butler county. The Fairview, Delamater, and Burns are enormous wells. Scarcely less remarkable is that near Larkin's mill, on Bull creek, south of Butler, and now used by Messrs. Spang, Chalfant & Co. and Graff, Bennet & Co., of Pittsburg. This well was sunk, 7 inches in diameter, to the "first sand rock," at a depth of 1150 feet. No oil was struck, but gas was furiously ejected, and was allowed to escape after tubing the well with a 5⅝-inch casing. The gas has a pressure of about 120 pounds at the well, and, while escaping, burned in a flame 15 feet in diameter and 40 feet long, with a noise like thunder. The heat developed was so great that constant spring reigned in the hollow in which the well is situated, grass and trees growing in February. (J. Cummings, signal service observer at Tarentum.) In 1875 the well was bought by the Natural Gas Company (limited), which laid a light lap-welded pipe, 6¼ inches internal diameter, and sunk 3 feet below the surface. The line ran almost direct for 17½ miles, from the well to Etna, on the Allegheny, and thence 2 miles further to Graff, Bennet & Co.'s mills. The volume of gas obtained is known to exceed 60,000 cubic feet per hour, for the pipe was filled and gas burned at Etna in less than 20 minutes after it was let on at the well. The actual volume is far greater, for it has just been discovered that during the construction some malicious person inserted a pump-log, bored with a 2-inch hole, into the pipe, about half way between its termini, yet, even with this obstruction, the line supplied Spang, Chalfant & Co.'s mill and about half the requirements of the Millvale works. The former mill was connected through a 4-inch pipe, out of which 75 half-inch connections ramified to all parts; 9 boilers and 36 furnaces (10 of them using gas alone) derived their supply from this pipe. The boilers and some of the furnaces use slack coal in addition, mainly to equalize combustion, for the grates and bridges remain unaltered. The gas is let in through a **T** and a pipe running cross-wise just over the outside end of the grate-bars, and pierced with numerous holes. The air is admitted and the furnace controlled by the damper, as usual, and a charge of 486 pounds gray forge and 100 pounds tap cinder is readily melted and boiled with gas alone in one hour and fifty minutes. When in use, the gas was burned at about 2 pounds per square inch; but, when shut off, the pressure rapidly rises as high as 80 pounds.

The gas from the "Harvey," *i.e.*, the well of the Natural Gas Company, has the following characteristics, determined by Prof. Sadtler, for the Geological Survey:—

I. Composition :

Carbonic acid, ...	0.66
Carbonic oxide, ...	trace.
Illuminating hydro-carbons, (?) . . .	trace.
Hydrogen, ...	13.50
Marsh gas (C. H.^{4}), ...	80.11
Ethyl hydride (C.^{2} H.^{6}), ...	5.72
Nitrogen, ...	. . .
Oxygen, ...	. . .
	99.99

II. Calorific value, 1.5597 calorific units.

Theoretical temperature of combustion, 2763°
centigrade.

III. Specific gravity, 0.5119.

The specific gravity of these gases seems to be heavier than that given above, or rather there may be gases of different specific gravities. In a well or tank natural gas will remain quiescent, and, when displaced, is seen flowing over the side like carbonic acid gas. When Messrs. Kirk & Dilworth secured the Burns and the Delamater wells, Dr. Otto Wuth reported to them that the specific gravity of the gas was 1.56. This question of composition and specific gravity has an important bearing on the value of the gas as fuel. A company has been recently formed to conduct gas from these wells into Pittsburg, so that the matter will soon be put to a practical test.

The use of natural gas has proved entirely successful. An exhaustive examination of its effects as fuel by the Geological Survey of Pennsylvania shows that used alone in the present furnaces it has a tendency to allow more phosphorus to remain in the iron, owing to a want of perfect combustion. For heating, the gas is a perfect fuel, causes little waste, and consequently protects the furnace bottoms, while the transparency of the flame allows the heater to see each pile at any time. The quantity issuing from a half-inch pipe suffices to heat up and supply a puddling or heating furnace. As to the permanency of the supply, it seems clear that if the wells now used are allowed to stand isolated, in tracts otherwise undeveloped, the supply will be lasting. But there is little doubt that if other wells are sunk around them for oil or gas the supply will gradually diminish and cease as it has already done in the great gas-wells at Titusville and in the East Sandy district.

ARMSTRONG COUNTY, formed in 1800 of parts of Allegheny, Westmoreland, and Lycoming. It lies within the Sixth or Freeport basin of the bituminous coal formation, and contains limestone and coal-measure ores. The coals are included mainly in the Lower or Allegheny series, which is bounded on the west by the conglomerate of Warren, Venango, and Mercer, and to the east by an axis of elevation stretching from Smethport nearly direct to Pittsburg. There are eight seams in all, the upper four of which, especially the Upper and Lower Freeport and Kittanning veins, are the most valuable. The Upper Freeport vein is persistently underlaid by the Freeport limestone, and a bed of calcareous iron-ore underlies the limestone. At the Great Western or Brady's Bend furnaces, 2 miles from the mouth of Sugar creek, the coal is 4½ to 6 feet thick, the limestone 5 feet, and the ore or "Summit Vein" 2 to 2½ feet, or even 4 feet thick (Phillip's Hill). This ore is compact, very argillaceous, and remarkably like the Big Bottom ore of Connellsville and Uniontown; it is mined in gangways and by stripping, but will not bear a greater amount of stripping than 20 feet. It yields at Brady's Bend 1½ tons to the yard, averages 3 to 3¼ tons to the ton of metal, and cost in 1865 $2.15 per ton of 2480 pounds to mine, and 16 cents per ton to calcine it. The Lower Kittanning coal-bed or furnace-bed, with about 3½ feet of coal, was mined at the furnaces, and about 20 feet below it, and some 140 feet below the summit ore, occurs the silicious Slab ore representing the " Buhr-stone" ore of Clarion, Venango, and neighboring counties. Below this lies a ferriferous limestone,—the so-called Fossiliferous Limestone of the lower coal measures. This bed is quarried for flux on both sides of the Sugar Creek valley near the furnaces.

In 1828 the *Kittanning Gazette*, October 25th, enumerated 3 charcoal furnaces, viz., Bear Creek, Allegheny (1827), and Rock (1825), and no forges; the product went down the Allegheny to Pittsburg. Bear Creek furnace was said to be the largest in the country, making, when in blast, forty tons per week; it had been out of blast for some time. The Allegheny furnace, on west side of the river, 2 miles above Kittanning, made 14 to 15 tons per week, while the Rock furnace, on the Kiskiminetas and the Pennsylvania Canal, made 15 to 20 tons a week.

In 1840 the county had three furnaces, which produced 1034 tons of iron. Day enumerates the Bear Creek and Allegheny furnaces and the Great Western furnace, rolling-mill, and nail-works. The latter, afterwards Brady's Bend, were built in 1840 and 1841, by Philander Raymond, to be run on Welsh systems of work, and made a large quantity of *rails*.

These iron-works were remarkable in several ways, as being among the first to make rails, and from the fact that the poor success of their first larger furnaces fixed 12-foot boshes as the favorite size for coke-furnaces. The *first coke iron* was made in Fayette and Clearfield counties, but the result was such that the Lonaconing furnace was considered, thirty years ago, as the first entirely successful coke-furnace in the United States. It was built by the George's Creek Company in 1837, and commenced in 1839 to make iron. It afterwards had as managers Alexander & Co., Detmold and Overman, successively, but lack of transportation was fatal to it. The Mount Savage and Great Western furnaces were exact copies of it (Overman), but while at Lonaconing good foundry iron was made this was seldom the case at the other furnaces, the Great Western making only red-short white forge iron, owing, it was said, to the extremely sulphurous character of the coal. Inexperience, however, was probably the actual cause, for though the ores are lean the coal should have made fair coke. The dimensions were 15 feet at the boshes, 50 feet high; there was little or no actual hearth, but the lower part of the boshes tapered down to the tuyeres; the stack was a stone one 50 feet square at the base and 25 feet square at the top. In 1848 the furnaces were blown through 6 tuyeres, with hot blast, and made 70 to 80 tons of iron per week.

It will be most interesting to describe the rolling-mill in Mr. Raymond's own language; he wrote a long letter concerning it, in 1844, to Mr. Buffington, a representative in Congress, in answer to an inquiry as to the quantity of railroad iron that could be furnished in the United States. "These (Great Western) works alone are capable of turning out of finished railroad iron 125 tons per week. We are now manufacturing rails for several companies. That which has been tried of our make is found to be superior to the best articles imported from England. * * * * H, T, and U rails, or any other patterns in use, can be made for $50 per ton. The expenses of transportation to the lakes will be not more from the works than from Pittsburg. The cost of transportation from the works to Cincinnati and to Madison, Indiana, has been $2.50 per ton; iron can now be transported for $2 to same points. The H, T, and U rails can be made from 9 to 18 feet long, according to the weight per foot. The works can be enlarged in a short time to a capacity to make (of finished railroad iron of any pattern required) 200

tons per week, if a market can be found for the iron.
* * * * The two blast-furnaces are capable of
producing 100 tons of metal per week each. The rolling-mill has 12 puddling-furnaces of a capacity to make
2 tons of iron per day each, and 1 scrap and 3 balling
furnaces for merchant mill or finishing rolls. Attached
is a nail-factory capable of manufacturing 3 tons per day
of assorted nails; also, sheet and boiler plate rolls, and
a forge with hammer, squeezers, roughing and puddle
bar rolls. * * * In addition to the Brady's Bend
there are several large iron establishments; Mt. Savage
and the Danville works you doubtless are acquainted
with." (Niles' Reg., Feb. 1st, 1845.)

In July, 1845, Thomas Chambers stated the capacity
of the Great Western works at "5000 tons half railroad"
(? rerolled), and of the Mt. Savage at "5000 tons of
railway iron." In reference to the first rails made, Danville began in November, 1845, Phœnixville in November, 1846, and Safe Harbor in 1848. Horace Gray
made rails at Pembroke, Maine, at an early date.

In 1856 the county had three furnaces, producing
1034 tons; 1 rolling-mill, with a product of 2500 tons,
and 1 rail-mill, which made 7533 tons of rails.

In 1873 it had 11 coke-furnaces, which produced
22,260 tons of coke pig; 3 rolling-mills, with a product
of 5000 tons, and 1 idle rail-mill, the Brady's Bend
works, then in bankruptcy.

BEAVER COUNTY, formed in 1800 out of parts of
Allegheny and Washington counties. It lies in the
bituminous coal formation, in the Sixth basin. The
Upper or Monongahela measures come over the
southern line of the county; the hills rising between
the Conequenessing creek and Beaver river consist of
the barren measures, the Upper and Lower Freeport

cropping out irregularly in the hollows. West of the Beaver all the coals above the Brookville are present, but only at Industry have they been hitherto reliable. There the Kittanning bed supplies coal of a superior quality.

Hoopes, Townsend & Co. built a charcoal-furnace in 1803, at Brighton, near Beaver Falls, which was abandoned not long after; since that time the county has done nothing of which record remains. Recently, however, Messrs. Able, Pedder & Co., the senior partners of which had long been associated with Singer, Minick & Co., organized the Beaver Falls Steel Company, and erected, in 1875, a rolling-mill with gas furnaces and an open-hearth steel furnace, the ingots from which are reduced to billets on a 16-inch train. At the opening, the Beaver Falls Cutlery Company, of some note as employing Chinese, presented the steel company with half a dozen finished table knives, made from its steel, one hour and a quarter after it had been rolled.

BEDFORD COUNTY, formed in 1771 out of Cumberland. This county contains all measures, from the Upper Silurian limestone of (II.) to the coal-bearing strata (XIII.). At Broad Top mountain, in the north-eastern corner of the county, an isolated coal basin, of the same name, forms the mountain, including the whole series of coals above the conglomerate to the Pittsburg bed, a mere patch of which remains. The coal mined is semi-bituminous, with about 17½ per cent. of volatile matter; it is coal of good quality, but less bituminous than that west of the Allegheny mountains.

In this county the fossil ore of the Upper Silurian red shales (Clinton or No. V.) is highly developed in each variety, the soft, as well as the hard ore in connection with the Iron sandstone. In the Bedford region the soft fossil ore is mined, along Dunning's creek, on Dunning's mountain, in *three* beds, with an average total of 3 to 4 feet of ore, yielding somewhat under 50 per cent. Above the fossil bands and on the Heldenberg limestones brown hematite has been extensively mined for the old Hopewell furnaces. Below the Umbral shales at Hopewell is a brown argillaceous 50 per cent. ore. The "Levant" iron-ore, about 700 to 1000 feet below the fossil ore, crops out along the east slope of Tussey in variable thicknesses, being sometimes found 20 feet thick. It is divided into beds of different color, the upper bed, heavy purple block ore, containing about 40 per cent. of iron, and the soft middle bed about 47 per cent. The latter makes the best iron, though most of these ores have, of course, a marked tendency to cold-shortness. The two 14-foot furnaces of the Kemble Iron Company at Riddlesburg have been very successful in using washed coal coked and the county ores.

In 1829 there were 2 furnaces, each making 25 to 30 tons of pig per week, and 6 forges, which averaged each 250 tons of bar iron a year.

In 1856 there were 1 charcoal-furnace, making 700 tons, and 2 forges, the product of which was 600 tons of bars and blooms.

In 1873 the county had 1 charcoal-furnace (Hopewell, 1800), which made 903 tons, and 2 coke-furnaces, which made 14,731 tons of pig iron. They belonged to the Kemble Iron and Coal Company. The forges had disappeared.

BERKS COUNTY, formed in 1752 of parts of Philadelphia, Chester, and Lancaster counties. The county contains the Mesozoic red sandstone and the red shales of the secondary series, the primary rocks of the South mountain, and the limestone of the Kittatinny valley, bounded to the west by the "Matinal" slates (Utica), and shales (Hudson river slate). Several distinct regions of ore are observed. East of and in the South mountain chain magnetic ore has been long and extensively mined; recent explorations at Seeholzville and Boyerstown have proved important deposits. At Boyerstown one of the best ores in the State, a hard, calcareous, magnetic ore, free from phosphorus, has been long mined by the Eckert and Reeves firms, on a vein varying in thickness from a few inches to 20 feet, and exactly resembling the Penn's Mount and Island vein at Reading. Recent borings seem to show an enormous thickening of this bed toward its dip. In the East Pennsylvania valley brown hematite is very extensively mined over the Matinal slates, the Moselem being the oldest and largest single bank. From Mertztown to Fogelsville is an important district from which the Lehigh furnaces are supplied. West of the Schuylkill, ore has been less extensively mined. The Robesonia furnaces use Cornwall ore, but the Jones mine of magnetic ore, occurring in primary rocks at the southern edge of the red sandstone belt, has been long worked for charcoal furnaces on the Schuylkill. The Schuylkill group of furnaces is included in the counties of Montgomery, Chester, and Berks.

Ebeling states, on Schopf's authority, in 1797, that about 1795 there were 4 furnaces at work in the county, viz., Udree's furnace, 2 miles from Reading, with a forge making 200 to 300 tons, and mines in the Oley mountains, where 6 men were employed in 1783; the old Redding started *again* in 1792 with a forge, and often remained in blast 18 months,—a surprising thing in 1790; Bird's and Patton's, and also 10 forges. The forges were, in addition to those mentioned, Pine,

Lesher's or Rutter's, on the Manathanim (Manatawny), an old forge, using rich but red short-ore and working it mixed with "Chester ore" into bars; Sands, Spring, Douglas, Lewis Richards in Colebrookdale and Oley's. Scull marks 16 forges on his map.

The Pool forge, built by Thomas Rutter, on the Manatawny, not far from Pottstown, was probably the first forge in the vicinity, and is said to have been unsuccessfully attacked by Indians in 1728.

The early date of the Mount Pleasant furnace has been already mentioned, but the details of its first blasts, as supplied by the papers of the Potts family, are worthy of attention.

Account Pig Metal and other Castings made at Mount Pleasant Furnace during the following Blasts, viz. :

	Tons.	Cwt.	Qrs.	Lbs.
First blast, commencing October 12th, .				
1738. Hove off December 11th,				
Made the said blast, pigs, . .	85	0	0	0
Country castings, ...	6	1	2	2
Fforge castings, ...		7	3	6
	91	9	1	8

	Tons.	Cwt.	Qrs.	Lbs.
Second blast, commencing March 14th,				
1738–39. Hove off July 12th, 1739.				
Made the said blast, pigs, . .	173	14	3	0
Fforge castings, ...		10	2	0
	174	5	1	0

	Tons.	Cwt.	Qrs.	Lbs.
Third blast, commencing October 22d, 1739. Blowed out December 14th, 1739. Made the said blast, pigs, ...	92	6	1	24
Country castings, ...	5	14	0	23¾
Fforge castings, ...	1	10	1	19
	99	11	0	10¾

(A short blast, from August 28th to September 7th, 1739, included in yᵉ above.)

	Tons.	Cwt.	Qrs	Lbs.
Fourth blast, commencing March 3d, 1739–40. Blowed out May 26th, 1740. Made the said blast, pigs, .	153	10	0	0
Country castings, ...	8	3	2	7
Fforge castings, ...	1	5	1	14
	162	18	3	21

	Tons.	Cwt.	Qrs.	Lbs.
Fifth blast, commencing August 28th, 1740. Blowed out November 16th. Made the said blast, pigs, ...	86	10	0	0
Country castings, ...	12	3	0	3½
Fforge castings, ...		13	3	0
	99	6	3	3½

	Tons.	Cwt.	Qrs.	Lbs.
Sixth blast, commencing May 18th, 1741. Blowed out July 20th. Made the said blast, pigs, . . .	60	0	0	0
Country castings, ...	2	4	0	15
Fforge castings, ...	1	2	2	1
	62	6	2	16

In 1831 two exact surveys, aided by returns from the works, showed 11 charcoal-furnaces, averaging 4470 tons of pig iron and 1195 tons of castings yearly, and 23 forges, averaging yearly 2053 tons of bar iron and 1716 tons of blooms. This work was done by Messrs. J. U. Schneider and Simon Seyfert, men of local experience, for the convention of Friends of American Industry, held at New York in 1831. The tables they give are so interesting, showing the state of the trade at that time in one of the principal iron districts of the country, that we reproduce them on pages 156 and 157, but omit the columns relating to the families of workmen and to the number of horses employed; 2767 hands were directly employed, whose families numbered 14,516 souls; 1630 horses were used in the work of manufacture.

Mr. Prevost states that founders were paid, if they had one or two boys, $1000 a year; wood-choppers, 35 cents per cord, and wagoners $100 to $120 a year and their board.

Joanna furnace, like most of the furnaces in this region, cast hollow ware, and Jones, Keim & Co., at Windsor, made excellent artistic castings of all kinds, being the first founders in America to make perfect castings of that description. George Keim cast in sand, direct from the furnace, a copy of the Last Supper, after Da Vinci; he also made many excellent busts of individuals one of which, quite remarkable for the perfection of its execution, is preserved in the museum of the American Philosophical Society at Philadelphia.

In 1856 Berks produced 8998 tons of pig iron, in 10 charcoal-furnaces, and 9 anthracite-furnaces made 25,524 tons; 20 forges produced 3407 tons of blooms, &c.

In 1873 there were 5 charcoal-furnaces, which made 4095 tons; 18 anthracite-furnaces, which made 79,515

Furnaces in Berks County in 1828, 1829, and 1830.

Furnaces.	Owners.	Workmen directly employed during three years.	Cords of Wood consumed during three years.	Tons of Pig Iron made during three years.	Tons of Castings made during three years.
Reading, ...	George Ege, ...	228	23,822	3,568	95
Hopewell, ...	Buckley & Brooke, . . .	168	15,000	1,000	700
Joanna, ...	William Darling, ...	168	15,000	1,200	500
Mount Penn, ...	Seyfert & Schwartz, . . .	220	15,000	1,700	500
Oley, ...	J. U. Schneider, ...	150	10,500	1,050	360
Sally Ann, ...	J. V. R. Hunter, ...	150	10,800	1,300	252
Mary Ann, ...	Reuben Trexler, ...	153	12,000	1,350	330
Windsor, ...	Jones, Keim & Co., . . .	195	11,200	650	750
Moselem, ...	N. V. R. Hunter, ...	18	4,500	643	. .
Union, ...	George Reagan, ...	18	6,000	700	. .
Keimville, ...	Jones, Keim & Co., . . .	12	4,500	250	100
				13,411	3,587

Given by A. M. PREVOST, April, 1832.

Forges in Berks County in 1828, 1829, and 1830.

Forges.	Owners.	Workmen directly employed during three years.	Cords of Wood used during three years.	Tons of Bar Iron.	Tons of Bloom.
Charming,	George Ege,	99	9,006	800	1,900
Giberaltar,	Seyfert & Schwartz,	168	9,000	...	1,000
Dowell,	Jonathan Seidel,	85	5,000	...	600
Sixpenny,	George Zacharias,	62	3,000	...	...
Birdsborough,	Heirs of M. Brooke,	94	7,500	750	300
Speedwell,	Daniel Yocem,	99	3,450	205	...
North Kill,	B. & J. Seyfert,	36	3,000	300	...
Green Tree,	Keen & Burkart,	19	1,600	150	750
Moselem (2),	N. & J. Hunter,	110	7,500	300	...
Rockland,	J. U. Schneider,	53	4,500	450	600
Union,	George Reagan,	61	3,000	...	...
Spring,	J. S. Bartolette,	41	3,750	375	...
Oley,	J. S. Sprang,	35	3,000	300	...
New District,	W. Schall,	30	3,000	240	...
District (2),	Reuben Trexler,	62	5,300	480	...
Mt. Pleasant,		93	9,600	720	...
Dale,	D. Schall,	32	3,100	240	...
Rockland,	D. Oyster,	18	2,500	150	...
Pine,	J. Rutter,	90	8,500	700	...
				6,160	5,150

A. M. PREVOST, 1832.

tons; 9 rolling-mills, with a product of 15,756 tons; 1 rail-mill (Reading Railroad), which made 21,221 tons, and only 3 forges, with a product of 600 tons of blooms.

BLAIR COUNTY, formed in 1846 of parts of Huntingdon and Bedford. The county lies mainly between the crest of Tussey mountain and the western slope of the Alleghenies. Its main geological feature is a lower Silurian valley, running through the country between Dunning's, Lock, Canoe, Brush, and Bald Eagle mountains on the west, and Tussey mountain to the east.

On the Tussey mountain the fossil ore outcrops, as in Bedford county. To the west of Dunning's mountain lies an upper Silurian valley, in which fossil ore occurs on the western and northern slopes of Dunning's, Lock, and Canoe mountains in the "Hatchet" Cove. Near Frankstown it has been largely mined, on the south-east slope of Tussey, by the Cambria Iron Company, in a three-bench bed 15 to 25 feet thick. In the Canoe valley the "barrens" form a double ridge in Morrison's Cove, with brown hematite in the northern ridge. The Springfield and Bloomfield furnaces use this ore.

It is believed that the first blast-furnace in Pennsylvania, or in the country, to utilize its gases for steam, &c., was the Elizabeth furnace, in this county. It did so in 1836. It was built in 1832, having a height of 32 feet and a 9-foot bosh, and with the same dimensions was blown in as a coke-furnace in 1872. It used, doubtless, the flame from the tunnel-head, not the uninflamed gas drawn from below the mouth of the furnace. It is quite certain that the first furnace to do this latter was the Greenwood, in Orange county, New York, owned by Mr. Parrot. This method of procuring unburnt gas is due to Faber du Faur, of Wasseralfingen in

Würtemberg, and was patented in this country by Mr. C. E. Detmold as his agent, in 1842 and 1845. Through an inaccurate patent specification Mr. Detmold lost the profit of the improvement. There is no doubt, however, that to his skill and energy we are indebted for the economical use of waste gases in this country. He introduced Faber du Faur's methods of collecting and burning the waste gas under hot-blast stoves and boilers at the Phillipsburg (then Cooper) furnaces, at the Crane Iron works, at the Cedar Point and Chesapeake furnaces in Baltimore, at the Harford furnace, Ashland Iron-works, and in other places, all before 1850.

Faber du Faur, in 1832, had devised an apparatus for heating blast, so good that it was generally used under the name of the Wasseralfingen stove, and placed it at the tunnel-head of the furnace, conducting the gas and flame from near the top of the mouth through a cast-iron pipe into the stove. This method he subsequently improved by taking the gas, in 1836, at a lower depth in a pure, uninflamed state, using it for puddling. Faber du Faur thus added a *new idea* to blast-furnace practice, viz., that there was a point at which the gas had done its work, and at which it could be safely taken in an uninflamed state for subsequent use. Ebelmen demonstrated this afterward scientifically, by analysis of the gases; but it was held for a long time subsequently that the gas had not done its work till it had escaped at the mouth of the furnace. Consequently, no rational hot-blast stoves could be built or, if built, *preserved from destruction* by occasional intense heat succeeded by a sudden cooling. Faber du Faur proved this disastrous notion false, and showed that to burn the gas well (as stated by Ebelmen) it should have little or no vapor of water, be burnt in a contracted space at the end of the flue, and proved that the supply of gas could be rendered independent of the charges. Thus treated, the gas gives out an amount of heat vastly beyond that of its temperature on escaping from the furnace.

Mr. Stephen Colwell stated, in a deposition taken in 1851, that furnaces did not then usually take uninflamed gas, but "the proper proportion of atmosphere is (was) taken into the flues with the gases," which were not conducted pure and unburnt to the place of combustion, nor were they taken out "8 or 10 feet below the mouth of the furnace, where the fuel is in a state of full combustion;" that iron men in 1840 did not understand the saving of waste heat to be a real combustion of the gases, hence had at one time a hot and at another "a cold flame," and they mistrusted the European experiments because they thought them "scientific"! About 1840 to 1845 our furnaces began to take gas lower down, say 1 ½ to 6 feet from the mouth, but the effect of this was stated to be not to prevent a mixture of air with the gas, but to lessen the quantity thus mixed and prevent too rapid combustion "not only outside but in the flues." All this is stated as the result of personal experience, and of the contemporary examination of American furnaces to suggest improvements for a new construction. What a fearful state of things to modern eyes!

Mr. Detmold has employed the waste gases for refining pig iron in a reverberatory furnace, using a blast to convert the pig into "run-out or plate metal." This was done successfully, so far as product and quality was concerned, at the Danville furnace, in Dauphin county, the Harford furnace, and at the Crane Iron works, at the instance of Mr. David Thomas. But the blowing-tubs, driven by water-power, then employed, produced a blast insufficient for both the furnace and the refinery, so the latter was abandoned. Further, though Faber du Faur's method of puddling by means of a flame produced from waste gas, burnt by numerous jets of air forced into it, was never extensively followed in connection

with the blast-furnace, yet Mr. Detmold applied it to ordinary coal furnaces in a manner so successful that it is still used at some works. He
sunk the grate-bars, made a deep fire to produce as much carbonic oxide
as possible, which he burnt by forcing jets of hot or cold air into it in its
passage over the fire-bridge. This system was adopted at Bronton, New
Jersey; Saugerties, New York, and at nearly all the Massachusetts iron
works. I quote from *Fisher's Industrial Record* a letter describing the
working of these improvements at the Boonton Iron works;—

"BOONTON, December 12th, 1843.

"DEAR SIR:—I have just received yours and hasten to give you the
information you desire. I will give you the account of our work for the
last week:—

"There was charged to the double furnace, tons 30.15.0.24 pig and
plate; ¾ pig and ¼ plate, which produced, tons 29.11.2.24 pounds of
billets and bars, and consumed about 11 cwt. 2 qrs. of anthracite coal per
ton of bars produced. Five single furnaces, for the same time, averaged
each, tons 12.17.3.8 billets and bars, with about the same waste as the
double furnace—coal per ton 14 cwt., 2.10.

"The ball furnace produced, of heated iron, for the same week, 66
tons, viz., merchantable iron, band, large hoops and billets from blooms,
average waste 5½; coal, 5.3.18 per ton of iron produced. The refinery,
in the same time, produced 46 tons good metal, waste 6½; coal, 6.0.22
per ton of plate produced. With our old anthracite-furnaces the average
waste in puddling was about 6½. Average weekly product of our single
furnaces, tons 12¼ @ 12½ per week, coal being the same kind of anthracite as we now use, with 21 cwt. per ton of bars produced. In reheating
the waste was about 6½ and coal from 7 to 10 cwt. per ton, according to
the kind of work done.

"When I see you I can give you more minute information; and hoping
to have that pleasure in a few days, I am, &c.,

"HENRY BREVORT.

"C. E. DETMOLD, Esq."

In 1856 there were in operation in the county 9
charcoal-furnaces, with a product of 9831 tons of pig
metal; 4 coke-furnaces, making 6584 tons of pig; 1
rolling-mill, with a product of 1500 tons, and 10 forges,
which made 5772 tons of blooms and bars.

In 1873 there were 2 anthracite-furnaces, with a
product of 4300 tons; 9 coke-furnaces, which made

17,920 tons, and 3 charcoal-furnaces, which produced 4095 tons of pig iron; 4 rolling-mills made 4177 tons (including 132 tons of light rails), and 6 forges produced 3070 tons of blooms.

BUCKS COUNTY, one of the original counties of the province of Pennsylvania. The southern end of the county is occupied by gneiss and rocks of the primary formations which are overlapped, north of Attleboro and Rockville, by the new red formations, broken, in places, by dikes of trap, like Haycock Hill and the long dike in Marlborough township. These mesozoic red shale and sandstone formations occupy the rest of the county. Limestone occurs in narrow, isolated belts at Durham and east of Doylestown.

There has never been much ore mined in the county, except in the gneiss belt of the South mountains, at Durham. There both magnetic and red hematite ores have been won.

In this county lay the original Durham furnace, formerly described, with its forge. Scull marks on his map a "new furnace" and its forge, nearer the river, which, however, is mentioned neither by Howell nor Scott. Acrelius regarded Durham as the best iron-works in the country, because there was not "three-quarters of a mile hauling about the works, and a rich supply of ore, wood, and limestone."

The mine, situated on a high hill, is rich in good ore and forty feet deep. A furnace at the foot of the hill receives the ore. It may be regarded as the best iron-works in the country; has a rich supply of ore, wood, water, sand, limestone, &c. The ore is so near to the furnace, and the furnace so near to the forges, that there is not three-quarters of a mile of hauling about the works.

The forge lay about a mile and a half from the Delaware, on which the iron was taken to Philadelphia, for twenty shillings a ton, in the "Durham boats," which carried about 15 tons. In 1759 the owners of the Durham property were William Logan and Anthony Morris. The ore was silicious and refractory, and the works did not prosper.

There are now near the same spot 2 anthracite-furnaces, built by Cooper, Hewitt & Co., in 1848 and 1851, which used a great deal of New Jersey ore, and made 10,000 tons of pig iron in 1856, and in 1873, 9335 tons of pig iron. The iron made from Durham ore was extremely rich in silicon, containing over 5 per cent., and was sold for Bessemer iron, at a time when charcoal pig was mainly used, to increase the amount of silicon in the charge. These furnaces have recently been entirely rebuilt to make Bessemer iron from mixed ores.

There are no records of other works. The county has had only 1 forge, built at Bristol in 1844, for heavy forgings, and transformed into a rolling-mill, which made 1000 tons in 1873 (and has now been moved to New Castle, Delaware), and the Bristol Rolling-mill (1875), with 1 furnace and 2 trains of rolls.

BUTLER COUNTY, formed in 1800 of part of Allegheny. It lies in the bituminous-coal formation, the Sixth coal basin being here of great width, and coal-measure ores are developed to some considerable extent much in the same way as in Armstrong county.

In 1840 the county had 3 charcoal-furnaces, which made 625 tons of pig iron. In 1856 there were 4 charcoal-furnaces, with a product of 2010 tons. In 1873 all the iron-works had been abandoned. South of the petroleum district of this county, and also immediately in it, near Petrolia, are the great gas-wells previously described.

CAMBRIA COUNTY, formed in 1804 of parts of Huntingdon, Somerset, and Bedford. It lies in the bituminous-coal formation, in the wide tracts of the First basin, which, stretching from the western summit of the Alleghenies, ascend the eastern slope of Laurel Hill.

Coal is principally mined in the Stoystown and Johnstown subdivisions of the basin. In the region about Johnstown the Sharon coal is represented by a thin vein, and the Clarion and Freeport groups by veins of good thickness. The Brookville or the Clarion bed, the lowest, is 3½ feet thick at Johnstown. Above it lies the ferriferous coal-bed, with its limestone, each very variable, the coal from 1 to 4 feet and limestone 3 to 8 feet. The ferriferous limestone changes locally into carbonate ore. The Kittanning vein, thin at Johnstown, is 4 feet thick at other places. The Lower and Upper Freeport coals are respectively 4 feet on Laurel Hill creek and about 4 feet on the Conemaugh. The Pittsburg bed does not appear. Sixty feet over the highest coal is a double bed of compact carbonate ore, the upper band 18 inches to 2½ feet thick; the lower 6 inches to 2 feet; the total average thickness being 2 to 3½ feet of ore, containing about 51 per cent. of iron. This ore is smelted with local coke; but the Cambria Company depends largely on the brown hematites of Springfield, &c. and the fossil ores of Frankstown, Hollidaysburg, &c. For a better class of iron and for Bessemer pig iron Lake Superior ore is used.

Iron was made more than 60 years ago in a forge on Stony creek, afterward removed to a site in the present Millville borough. Ben's Creek charcoal-furnace was built in 1846 by George S. King & Co., and in 1856 made 902 tons. The Eliza furnace, at Ebensburg, was also erected in 1846. In 1856 there were 7 coke-furnaces at or near Johnstown, which made 22,697 tons of pig out of coal-measure ore, and the rail-mill of the Cambria Company, built in 1854. The latter was burnt in 1856, in which year it made 13,206 tons of rails; and was burnt again in 1872. Notwithstanding this misfortune it made in 1872 the largest production of any single works in the country, viz., 81,006 tons of iron and steel rails.

The Cambria Iron Company works were built when

Johnstown had about 2000 inhabitants, as the distributing port at the head of the western division of the Pennsylvania canal. They were at first dependent on the product of "4 *charcoal-furnaces*," which were enlarged and improved and then yielded a *product of 200 tons per week;* though 4 other coke-furnaces to smelt the local ore were nearly completed in 1855.

Dr. Shoenberger and George S. King were the originators. Like most American works the company failed on the completion of their construction, and were succeeded by a company of which Matthew Newkirk was president. This, too, suspended in 1855, and the works came by lease into the hands of Wood, Morrell & Co., Mr. Morrell, as manager, residing at Johnstown, and Messrs. Wood and Townsend conducting the general business. After surmounting many obstacles, and by a heavy investment of additional capital, the works were brought to a paying standard, and were incorporated in 1862 under the present title. The company now owns about 60,000 acres of coal lands in addition to the works described below.

The furnaces of the company were those commonly built for coke, 48 feet and 13 feet, and are located on a hillside. They produced white red-short iron from local ores and coke. Recently two fine stacks, 20 feet and 75 feet, have been built at Johnstown for Bessemer iron, and a stack at Conemaugh station (1857) rebuilt to make "Spiegeleisen." Foreign and domestic ores are mixed to produce an iron rich in manganese.

The mill originally built has been trebled in size since it was first burnt. Mr. John Fritz was the engineer of the leasing company, and to his mechanical skill is due an improvement since adopted by every rail-mill of the country—the *3-high* rail train.

This really consists of 2 pairs of rolls, the middle roll being the *top* roll of each pair, and the 3 rolls lengthened enough to receive the additional passes necessitated by inability to use the same *forming pass* on both sets of rolls. The uppermost roll is thus the bottom of the second set, and Mr. Fritz's invention consisted in arranging *hanging guards*, kept up against the roll by weights pulling vertically, and connected inside the fulcrum of the guard (or lever); also, in so forming the successive passes that a rail can be rolled always with the same side up (without turning over), and so that no seams or fins would be formed on the flanges. This was done by reducing the section somewhat at the point where, in the next pass, it is pressed against an opening between the *former* and the collars which make the *pass*. Further, a feeding-roller was arranged in front of each set of rolls, so to speak, to facilitate the introduction of the bar between the rolls. Thus no time was lost in returning the bar to the front of the rolls, as in the *2-high* sets, nor in turning the bar over, and the immediate effect of this was to increase the product over 30 per cent. In the usual 3-high rolls it is extremely difficult to roll an accurate rail section both halves of which shall be alike, as is required in Europe. In order to meet this difficulty, which in one case I have known to destroy a set of rolls in the course of adjustment, Mr. John Fritz has since, at Bethlehem, built an improved form in which the middle roll is fixed and the top and bottom roll accurately held and adjusted by stout screws, the whole so arranged that the rolls can be very easily changed.

At Johnstown, Mr. Fritz designed, in connection with James Moore, a vertical rolling-mill engine, direct-acting instead of the geared engines previously used, and short-stroke, with poppet-valves and adjustable cam governor. The dimensions of this engine were 30-inch cylinder and 26-inch stroke. Its usual speed was 85 revolutions per minute, but the stroke and power could be varied "by means of 3 holes in a solid steel disc instead of a crank." To keep the engine low the connecting-rod was forged like a fork, its two arms, joined below, working on a cross-head in guides bolted to the top of the cylinder. When this engine, driving the improved rolls, was started in 1855, a new epoch was begun in our rolling-mill engineering. Red shortness was a bugbear no longer, for pretty poor metal could be slipped through the rolls before it became weak, and, when cold, made a better rail. The Cambria rails have always been very superior, especially as regards *wear*.

The commercial management of the company has been very successful, and both by precept and by example it has long been one of the mainstays of the interests of American industry. The details quoted below give not only an idea of the local situation, but also of the rise caused by the war, and the vicissitudes of the iron trade.

Table of Costs.

Year.	Roasted ore, including expense mining, calcining, and waste.	Coal delivered in mill and at furnaces.	Pig Iron. Cost of production.
1860 and 1861.	$1 84	$0 67	$10 76
1864.	3 81	1 33	25 12*
1865.	4 31	1 54	31 31†
1875.	2 68	92	21 00

* Including Government tax from July, 1864, of $2, which equaled 77 cents on whole product.

† Including Government tax of $2.40 per net ton, increased to $2.48.

Table of Production.

Material.	1860—Tons.	1865—Tons.	1875—Tons.
Coal, tons mined, ...	152,155	148,789	190,847
Ore, tons mined, ...	124,530	76,729	60,613
Pig iron, tons made, . . .	26,484	17,606	21,436
Pig iron, tons bought, . .	10,333	15,538	56,673
New railroad bars, . . .	21,197	20,676	12,407
Rerolled railroad bars, . .	10,700	15,741	25,416
Steel rails, ...	. . . . . .	. . . . . .	42,326

Table of Wages.

Kind.	1860–61.	1864.	1865.	1875.
Day labor,	$0 70 per day	$1 45 per day	$1 56 per day	$1 10
Puddlers,	3 04 per ton	6 49 per ton	6 54 per ton	4 18
Rail-heaters,	33¾ "	69½ "	71¼ "	35$\frac{92}{100}$
Ore-miners,	85 "	1 68½ "	1 87½ "	1 20
Coal-miners,	32 "	78 "	82 "	48
Mechanics,	1 33 per day	2 70 per day	2 75 per day	2 00

Price of Iron Rails sold by Cambria Iron Company.

Year.	Lowest Price.	Highest Price.	Average Price on Total Sales.
1857.	$40 00	$63 50	$52 95
1858.	40 00	56 00	46 93
1859.	45 00	56 00	50 10
1860.	35 00	57 00	46 40
1861.	33 90	45 50	35 63
1862.	35 00	65 00	39 98
1863.	35 00	85 00	58 55
1864.	39 00	150 00	78 36
1865.	43 78	150 00	103 92
1866.	77 75	123 20	85 40
1867.	78 00	106 40	83 44
1868.	75 00	100 80	76 13
1869.	77 00	95 20	77 34
1870.	71 00	95 20	74 14
1871.	68 50	84 00	70 00
1872.	68 00	106 40	72 66
1873.	72 80	106 40	83 05
1874.	54 00	80 91	64 25
1875.	44 55	67 20	47 60

William Kelly, owner of the Suwaunee furnace, found that by plunging the noses of his tuyeres to some depth under the surface of the iron in the hearth, he could decarbonize or refine the iron to a great extent. The only change in this from the old European practice consisted in plunging the tuyere into the metal. But Kelly experimented in 1851 with what he called the "air-boiling" process, in order to supersede puddling. "My first efforts," he said, "were quite satisfactory; as with a blast taken from my furnace and introduced into a suitable cupola filled with liquid metal taken directly from the furnace, I produced a fair article of malleable iron. I found, when using gray iron, cold blast answered my purposes ; but when the metal was white, I found that hot blast had a better effect." In '1856 Mr. Kelly interested the Cambria Iron Company in his process, having taken out patents which gave his claims equal scope with those of Bessemer. An association was formed and experiments were made at Johnstown, in 1857, by Kelly, in a trial furnace. After various unsatisfactory experiments, a small cupola and a "low Bessemer vessel," to convert half a ton, were built in 1858. These experiments were unsatisfactory as to steel, but made a refined iron, which was puddled very economically. Mr. Kelly wrote, June 29th, 1858, " I have now fairly got it (the process) in successful operation at Cambria furnace, four miles from this place (Johnstown). It works well ; not the slightest difficulty in converting crude pig into refined plate metal by blowing into it for about 15 to 25 minutes. I have not consulted the manager, Mr. Fritz, as to the exact amount saved in the manufacture of rails, but I think it will be found somewhat like this :—

" Difference in puddler's wages, . . . $1 00
" 8 per cent. of increased weight on 1 ton of
    metal over the charge of crude pig @ $20, . 1 60
" 25 per cent. saved in fuel, fixings for furnace, &c., 50
" 1 reheat saved 50 cents ; 1 rerolling saved 50
    cents, ... 1 00
" 5 per cent. saved in loss of reheating and re-
    rolling (the iron at this stage being worth $25), 1 25
                                        ———
            "Total saving per ton, . . . $5 35

" I have no doubt that the above is nearly correct, the time saved in puddling a heat is about three-quarters of an hour. It makes a bar very different in quality from the crude pig."

Mr. J. Lowthian Bell has recently patented a process for removing silicon from pig iron intended for machine puddling (by means of a few minutes' exposure to the blast of a Bessemer vessel), which, if the published description be correct, *is identical with that of Kelly, even to the use of the Bessemer vessel as above.* It is Kelly's "air-boiling" treatment, by means of which he sold his "pig-blooms," in Cincinnati, for puddling, at a greatly enhanced price.

In 1871 the Bessemer steel-works of the company were completed. Previously, however, the first steel rails rolled on a regular order were rolled in the mill from small single-rail ingots made at the Pennsylvania Steel-works at Harrisburg. The Cambria Bessemer works were the second in the State, and are of design different from the other works, the Pennsylvania Steel Company and the Edgar Thomson representing the early designs, and the Bethlehem works a third construction. The Cambria works are built with the idea of making the Bessemer details independent of the walls of the building, which, with the roof, serve the purpose of an enclosure from the weather, and furnish the basis for the support of the hydraulic cranes which are on the usual Worthington designs. The converters, chimneys, cupola-ladles, cupolas, and spiegle-furnaces, are all mounted on columns and iron platforms supported on cast-iron girders sprung between the columns and fitting at the ends with a dovetail joint calked in with iron cement. Three levels are formed—the cupolas and spiegel-furnaces on the highest, the pig-iron ladles on the next, and the vessels and working-platform on the third and lowest level. The cupolas are supplied by a single-cylinder hydraulic-hoist, the stroke of the piston being half the lift. Blast is furnished the converters by two independent Fritz & Moore blowing-engines, in which the steam and blast cylinders are placed side by side on a common foundation, and the piston-rods are attached direct to a cross-head working over a fly-wheel on each side; the connecting-rods secure parallelism so easily that their brasses are scarcely worn, even after use for many years.

The largest product of Bessemer ingots these works have made is 297 gross tons in one day, 1475 gross tons in one week, and in the month of March last, 6051 gross tons. They are bloomed in a train of 30-inch rolls, 3 high, with box-grooves so proportioned that two or more passages may be made through the same groove, the top and bottom rolls being adjustable by screws worked by power. In the original mill of Mr. Holley the middle roll moved, and the top and bottom rolls were fixed. Mr. George Fritz invented a table, with feed-rollers, that could be raised and lowered by hydraulic power, the rollers being driven by power transmitted through double-rocking friction-gears, which come into gear in each position of the table at which the ingots enter the rolls. The ingots are turned over by their own weight, one corner being held up by a pusher (projecting between the rolls) while the table falls, and they are moved from one side of the table to the other by the same pusher. These feed-tables have been improved at Bethlehem, so that the feed-rolls may be driven in any position of the table. The Bessemer works and machinery form a monument to the late George Fritz fit to crown the career of any man.

In 1873 there were 9 coke-furnaces; 6 of them were built before 1854, 1 in 1857, 1 in 1874, and 1 building.

These made 30,000 tons of coke pig iron. The Cambria Works then contained a Bessemer works with two 5-ton converters, a blooming-mill for steel ingots, and 6 trains of rolls (25 sets). The trains are a 21-inch, an 18-inch, and a 12-inch rail-trains; 22-inch and 21-inch puddle trains, and a 16-inch merchant train. This is the largest works in this country. They made 28,479 tons of steel rails in 1873.

CARBON COUNTY, formed in 1843 of parts of Northampton and Monroe. The geological formations of the county range from the gray sandstones of formation IV. (Oneida conglomerate) to the coal measures; of these the county contains parts of the Southern, Beaver Meadow, and the lower ends of the southern Lehigh anthracite basins. The great mammoth vein is exposed 40 feet thick on the summit of Sharp mountain, west of Mauch Chunk. There is no workable iron-ore in this county.

The first anthracite iron was made in this county at Mauch Chunk, in 1838, by Baughman, Giteau & Co. A full description of the early iron manufacture with anthracite is appended to the description of Lehigh county.

In 1856 there were in the county 2 charcoal-furnaces, one of them (the Maria) built about 1753, rebuilt 1834. They made 1152 tons of pig iron. There were also 4 forges, which produced 258 tons of bars for home consumption.

In 1873 there were 1 charcoal-furnace, with a product of 675 tons, and 3 anthracite-furnaces, which made 2448 tons.

This furnace, Pennsville, 1837, now East Penn (John Balliet), is one of the few remaining cold-blast charcoal-furnaces in the country. It is now 28 feet high, 7½ feet bosh, 1¾ feet mouth, blown by water-power through a single 2½-inch tuyere. The charcoal-furnaces remaining in Carbon and Lehigh counties are usually in blast only seven or eight months in the year. They are run by farmers who in summer work their farms. The furnaces are on streams, to secure the water-power necessary to furnish blast, use only prepared ore and make a glassy cinder, all which one man can wheel away as it flows out.

CENTRE COUNTY, formed in 1800 of parts of Mifflin, Lycoming, Northumberland, and Huntingdon. The county includes the Lower Silurian limestone formations (II.) of the great valleys, east of the Bald Eagle mountain, with their brown hematite ores. Going thence north-westward all formations are met up to the coal measures. Bald Eagle mountain brings up sandstone IV. (Oneida), and on the western slope of the mountain are the Clinton (V.) formations with their fossil ores; the block ore associated with the Iron sandstone occurs of a rather silicious character. Limestone abounds. The brown hematite is the ore principally relied on, and reaches in Half-moon township its greatest development in the county. The fossiliferous limestones and sandstones, and the slates and sandstones of VIII. and IX., Upper Helderburg to Chemung series, carry here no special ores. Passing over the intermediate formations in the high ridge of the Allegheny mountain, we find the coal measures on its western slope, and high in the hills the bituminous coal-beds worked at Snow-shoe and Phillipsburg.

In 1828 there were 5 charcoal-furnaces at work making 6100 tons of pig iron yearly, and 4 more about to blow in; there were 7 forges, making 2800 tons of bar and blooms yearly; and 3 rolling-mills—Benner's,

Valentine's, and Thomas Miles'. In 1828 the Bald
Eagle furnace made its first blast under Mr. McCor-
mick; "it would clear $5000 in its first blast." In 1828
Centre county sent 800 tons of pig iron down the
Susquehanna on arks. The Logan's Gap furnace was
just built and the Centre, long idle, was about to start
again.

The pioneer of the iron trade in Middle Pennsylvania
was General Philip Benner, who was born in 1763, in
Chester county, and was brought up at Coventry forge.
He fought in the Revolution under Wayne and was
afterward highly successful in business at Coventry
forge. In 1792 he moved to Spring Creek, where he
built the first forge (Rock) in the county, afterwards
erecting the Rock furnace, another forge, and a rolling-
mill. When he went there the only market for iron was
on the Atlantic coast. But he struck out a new channel
of trade with Pittsburg, in iron and nails, packing his
products on mule-back, over almost impassable roads,
and bringing back salt in return. He called his iron
"Juniata iron," a brand (not relating to locality specially)
which became celebrated for good quality, and met no
competition for many years. The Centre furnace was
built in 1790 by one of the Curtins (Roland?) and the
Bellefonte forge in 1795. The Curtins, and the Valentine and Miles families, have largely controlled the iron
manufacture of the county.

The reputation of Juniata iron was well deserved.
The lower Silurian ores are very good in Pennsylvania
in the upper horizons, though in the *oldest strata* they are
quite cold-short. The limestone ores of our Lower
Silurian valleys make bar iron not inferior to that from
Salisbury (Connecticut) ore or to the best foreign iron.
The iron from this district of Centre, Mifflin, and

Huntingdon counties had been always used for best bar iron, and when puddled iron displaced the hammered bars, about 1840, the product of the district was used almost exclusively for the best boiler-plates.

The blooms for plate were made in a charcoal finery forge either from refined or light gray pig iron; in shape as a "block" 15 to 20 inches long and 5 to 9 inches in diameter, according to weight of plate desired. These blocks were reheated in a furnace with coal and drawn by a heavy hammer into slabs 2 to 3 inches thick. Most of the cinder was thus expelled, and the plate was rolled direct from the slab. It is so rolled yet, but only for the highest grade made. It was customary to make "piled iron" from the rough blooms without a second hammering; but, after rolling the blooms direct into bars an inch thick, these bars were cut and piled. It was usual before 1840 to make boiler-plate from iron refined in the "run-out" fire; to break up the plate or run-out metal into pieces, of a few pounds each, for the puddling-furnace, and to roll the puddled ball, after a slight hammering, direct into plate, or to roll it into broad bars for repiling. As compared with plate made direct from blooms, the piled plate was, in 1840, considered inferior. All plate now is made from "piles," whether from blooms or puddled, though, owing perhaps to early tradition, bars from blooms are sometimes put on top and bottom to make a smooth skin, filled inside with puddled bars. There is, however, now no reason why puddled iron plates should not be made as good as those made from charcoal blooms. Ordinary puddled plate may not flange as well nor be as ductile as the bloom iron; but it seems to wear as well in a boiler, and certainly appears to stand corrosion better.

In regard to the quality of these Juniata irons, the

report of a Committee of the Franklin Institute (on Materials for Steam-boilers), in 1837, is conclusive. It would be difficult to make tough iron softer.

Tensile Strength of "Juniata" Plate and Bar Iron.

	Pounds per square in.
Boiler-plate, Juniata blooms, " piled," Mason & Miltenberger, ...	56,081
Boiler-plate, Juniata blooms, " piled," Barnet Shorb, ...	45,914
Boiler-plate, Juniata blooms, " piled," Valentine & Thomas, ...	59,017
Boiler-plate, Juniata blooms, " hammered," Spang & Son, ...	57,365
Boiler-plate, Juniata blooms, " hammered," Shoenberger & Son, ...	53,803
Boiler-plate, Juniata·blooms, " hammered," H. Blake & Co., ...	59,607
Boiler-plate, puddled, H. Blake & Co., . .	51,039

Comparative Strength.

Bar iron,	Missouri, ...	49,909
"	Tennessee, ...	52,099
"	Salisbury, Connecticut, . .	58,009
"	Swedish, ...	58,184
"	Centre county, ...	58,400
"	Lancaster county, Messrs. Grubb, .	58,661
"	English cable iron, . . .	59,005

In 1842 there were on Bald Eagle creek 3 charcoal-furnaces; on Moshannon and Clearfield creeks 2 forges and a screw factory; on Spring creek 3 furnaces, 4 forges, 2 rolling-mills, and 1 nail-factory; on Fishing creek 3 charcoal-furnaces and 2 forges, and in the county 2 other charcoal-furnaces. In all, 13 charcoal-furnaces made 11,600 tons of pig iron; 10 forges made 4500 tons of blooms; and 3 rolling-mills made 2300 tons of bar iron and nails.

In 1849 1 hot-blast charcoal-furnace (Centre) made 1200 tons, and 6 cold-blast furnaces made 7660 tons, all out of brown hematite ores, there being 12 furnaces in all. Five forges existed, 4 of which made 1866 tons of blooms; and there were 5 mills, 4 of which (water-power) made 2746 tons of slit rod, bars, wire billets, and shovel-plate for the Philadelphia market.

In 1856 there were in the county 7 charcoal-furnaces making 7139 tons of pig; 5 forges, which made 2275 tons of blooms; and 5 rolling-mills, with a product of 4224 tons of blooms and bars.

In 1873 there were 4 charcoal-furnaces, which made 6001 tons; 1 coke-furnace and 4 rolling-mills, with a product of 4051 tons. A product of 4500 tons of blooms was reported, but only 1 forge is recorded.

CHESTER COUNTY, an original county of the province of Pennsylvania. Its formations are principally primary gneiss and metamorphic formations, the gneiss being overlaid in the north-eastern part of the county by New Red rocks (Mesozoic). In the latter formation, near its base, the old Warwick mines of magnetic ore occur, which have been wrought for 140 years. The Jones mine, also magnetic, appears at the junction of the primal sandstone with a belt of Lower Silurian lime-stone. In the serpentine belts of Chester and Lan-caster, chrome iron-ore occurs somewhat abundantly, and some titaniferous iron-ore. On the gneiss west of Phœnixville a quite rich, though limited, district of brown hematite in soil has been wrought. In the long limestone trough reaching from Abingdon, Montgomery county, into Lancaster county, much limestone brown hematite has been and is still raised. The proportions of dirt and ore vary from 3 parts dirt to 1 part ore in the easternmost localities to as little as 1 dirt to 2 ore west of Valley Forge and Coatesville. The county has a large total amount of ore, principally brown hematite, but in small deposits, necessitating a great deal of transportation.

This county, as described above, is the seat of the earliest iron-making in the State. In 1797 Ebeling enumerates 2 furnaces—the Warwick (which often made 40 tons a week, and was built by Nutt, who discovered the mines) and the Reading, and 6 forges which made yearly 1000 tons of bar iron.

In 1849, 3 anthracite-furnaces (Phœnix Iron Company, 1843, 1845, 1847) made 8025 tons of Nos. 2 and 3 iron; 6 forges (Mary Ann, 1785; Springton, 1790; Hibernia, 1792) made 1936 tons of blooms; and 14 rolling-mills made 11,826 tons of boiler and tube plate and rails (5463 tons), the rail-mill of the Phœnix Iron Company having been built and put in operation in the fall of 1846.

In 1856 Chester county had 1 charcoal-furnace, which made 750 tons of pig iron; 3 (Phœnix Iron Company) anthracite, which made 16,600 tons; 6 forges, which produced 706 tons of blooms; 10 rolling-mills, with a product of 10,099 tons, and 1 rail-mill (Phœnix Iron Company), which in that year made 18,592 tons of rails.

In 1873 there were in the county 1 charcoal-furnace, which made 710 tons; 3 anthracite, with a product of 10,440 tons; 11 rolling-mills, which made 21,385 tons, including 264 tons of light rails; and 4 forges, which made 2305 tons of blooms.

It is remarkable that the Isabella furnace, converted into a forge in 1853, should now have been resuscitated as the only charcoal-furnace in the county, and the old Warwick, believed to have been in operation for part of every year from 1736 till the Civil War, should have been broken up, its mines sold to the Phœnix Company, and even its name taken for an anthracite-furnace near Pottstown. But in this district the blast-furnace has always been associated with the forge, so when the forges were destroyed by cheaper iron, the charcoal-furnaces of the district had no market, since foundries using cheaper pig iron had monopolized their stove business, which was so old that even Franklin had furnished a design invented by himself.

Some of our oldest mills are in this county : the old Rokeby, built at Coatesville in 1795 ; the Brandywine, now Lukens' mill, also at Coatesville, 1810; and the mill of the Phœnix Iron Company, built in 1790, rebuilt in 1836, and a rail-mill added in 1846.

It is an important fact that the Lukens mill was the *first plate-mill* in the United States; it was, too, the only iron-mill that has been regularly managed by a lady, Mrs. R. M. Lukens. Mr. Charles Huston has kindly furnished me the facts for the following account of it :—

Jesse Kersey built the old rolling and slitting mill, was succeeded by Isaac Pennock, whose son-in-law, Dr. Charles Lukens, afterward became associated in the concern. Both partners dying, Mrs. Lukens conducted the business very successfully till she resigned it to her sons-in-law, Charles Huston and Charles Penrose, Jr. The mill early began to make boiler-plate by drawing down charcoal blooms into slabs as thin as possible, repeating these, on a bed of glowing charcoal, for rolling

into plates ¼ inch to 3/16 inch thick, which were shipped
to the boiler-maker. Several shipments of these plates
were sent to England for building some of the first loco-
motives. In the course of improvement anthracite coal
was substituted for charcoal, the plates were sheared,
the scrap worked up into nails; then the use of heating
furnaces greatly reduced the cost by making it possible
to 'pile,' and thus avoid the costly forging of the slab
under a comparatively light tilt-hammer at the forge.
The old mill stood where the puddle-mill now stands;
a change symbolical, perhaps, of the extent to which
the puddling-furnace has displaced the finery forge.

The first anthracite-furnace of the Phœnix Iron Company, described in the table under Lehigh county, cost,
exclusive of wheel-house and dwellings, $7949. It
made a cold-short iron from silicious ore from Yellow
Springs, yielding 38.3 per cent., with about 1.8 tons of
anthracite, but experienced great trouble from burning
out of hot-air pipes and destruction of hearth, apparently from insufficient blast. The mills have made
steady progress through almost all varieties of manufacture, at first boiler-plate and bar, then rails and
beams, and now principally beams, shapes, and bar
iron. Of late the Phœnix Iron Company has ceased to
make rails, and in 1874 has finished an extensive new
mill; the old mill had 8 trains of rolls, the new one
will have more than that number. The iron made is
used in engineering and architectural work, mainly by
the company itself, which has one of the most perfect
bridge-building works in the country. Great attention
is paid to quality and strength of the iron made, and
the designs for beam piles and composite columns are
very good. Mr. S. J. Reeves was the inventor of columns or tubes, not rectangular, built of sections riveted

together by flanges rolled on the section. Thus a given section can be used for columns of different diameters and of great lateral strength, owing to the stiffness of the flanges.

Mr. S. J. Reeves made in 1850 the following highly interesting statement concerning the *elements of the cost* of producing bar iron:—

Elementary cost of making a ton of Pig Iron on the Schuylkill River, at the Furnaces situated between Norristown and Spring Mills.

DATA.

2⅔ tons of iron-ore delivered at furnace, at $2 per ton, ...		$5 33
2 " of coal in the furnace, ⎫		
¼ " extra for steam, smith fires, &c., ⎬ 2¼, at $3.25, ...		7 31
1 " limestone, at 75 cents, ...		75
		$13 39
Furnace labor, ...	$2 00	
Other expenses, labor, wear and tear, superintendence, interest, &c., .	2 11	
		4 11
		$17 50

IRON-ORE.

Ore-leave,		40 cents per ton, at 2⅔ tons, ...	$1 06		
Mining,	$1 00		"		$2 67
Hauling,	50		"		1 33
Weighing, &c.,	10		"		27
	$1 60+40				$1 06+$4 27=$5 33

COAL.

Rent, ...		35 cents at 2¼ tons,	$0 78¾				
Operator's profit, ...		18 "	"	40½			
Mining, ...	90 cents,		"		$2 02½		
Charges on lateral roads, at							
25 cents, ...	13 "	12 "	"	27		29¼	
Wear and tear, 15 cents, . , . .	12 "	3 "	"	6¾		. 27	
Incidental labor, ...	7 "		"			15¾	
Reading Railroad, $1.30, . .	70 "	60 "	"	1 35		1 57½	
Interest, ...		5 "	"	11¼			
	$1 92	$1 33			$2 99 + $4 32 = $7 31		

LIMESTONE.

Quarry-leave,		10 cents at 1 ton, ...	10				
Quarrying,	25				25		
Hauling,	40				40		
	65	10		10 +	65	=	75

GENERAL EXPENSES.

Furnace labor, ... $2 00

Other labor and expenses, ... $1 00 + 1 11

$1 00 + $3 11 = $4 11

Forward ore, ... 1 06 + 4 27 = 5 33

" coal, ... 2 99 + 4 32 = 7 31

" limestone, ... 10 + 65 = 75

$5 15 + $12 35 = $17 50

The above shows the amount of labor represented by a ton of pig iron to be $12.35, and the amount of other items, not labor, composed of profits paid for the privilege of mining the minerals, coal-operators' profits, and interest on investments, &c., to be $5.15.

Every anthracite-furnace thus situated, making 5000 tons of metal per annum, will benefit the following interests thus :—

Clear profits to the Reading and other lateral railroads, for transporting coal to furnace, ... $1 62 | $8,100

Rent to owners of coal lands, ... 78½ | 3,925

Profit to the coal operators, ... 40½ | 2,025

Ore-leave to owners of ore lands, ... 1 06 | 5,300

Quarry-leave to owners of limestone quarries, ... 10 | 500

Capitalists and storekeepers, ... 1 18 | 5,900

$5 15 | $25,750

Laborers engaged in mining and transporting, &c., and about the works, ... 12 35 | 61,750

$17 50 | $87,500

Transportation to market, 75 cents, and drayage, 50 cents, ... 1 25 ⎫

Selling and guarantee commission, 5 per cent., ... 1 00 ⎬ 12,500

Storage, weighing, &c., ... 25 ⎭

5000 tons pig iron cost when sold, ... $20 00 | $100,000

5000 tons sold at present market price, ... 20 00 | 100,000

Profit to the manufacturer, ... 00 | 00

Analysis of the cost of Merchant Bar Iron manufactured on the Schuylkill River from Pig Iron costing $17.50 at the Mill.

DATA.

1⅓ tons of pig iron, at $17.50, ...	$23 38
2¼ tons of coal, at $3.25, ...	7 31
Labor per ton, ...	15 00
Interest, $1 ; wear and tear, $1 ; general expenses, $1.31, ...	3 31
	$49 00

INTERESTS BENEFITED.

	Furnace.	Rolling-mill.	TOTAL.
Stockholders of Reading and lateral roads, clear profits for carrying coal, in making 1⅓ tons pig iron, and in making bars, ...	$2 16	$1 62	$3 78
Rent to owners of coal lands, ...	1 04½	79	1 83½
Profit to coal operators, ...	54	41	95
Ore-leave to owners of ore lands, ...	1 41⅓	. . . .	1 41⅓
Quarry-leave to owners of limestone lands, ...	13⅓	. . . .	13⅓
Capitalists and storekeepers, ...	1 57⅓	2 31	3 88⅓
	$6 87 +	$5 13 =	$12 00

LABOR.

	Furnace.	Rolling-mill.	TOTAL.
Coal-miners and laborers, ...	$3 66	$2 75	$6 41
Labor for transporting coal, ...	2 10	1 79½	3 89½
Mining, hauling, &c., ...	5 69	. . . .	5 69
Quarrying and delivering limestone, ...	87	. . . .	87
Furnace labor, ...	4 14	. . . .	4 14
Mill labor and extra, ...	. . . .	16 00	16 00
	$16 46 +	$20 54 =	$37 00
Brought down, ...	6 87 +	5 13 =	12 00
	$23 33 +	$25 67 =	$49 00

Add transportation to market, ...	$1 00	
Porterage, &c., ...	50	
Commission and guarantee, 5 per cent. on $55, . .	2 75	
Charges, ...	50	
		4 75
		$53 75

CR.

By sales at $55 per ton, ...	55 00
Profit to manufacturer, ...	$1 25

Every complete establishment producing 10,000 tons of merchant bars per annum pays to diversified labor, at . . $37 00 per ton, $370,000

To owners of coal in the ground,.	1 83½	"	18,350
To the coal operator, clear profit, at	95	"	9,500
To the owners of ore lands for ore-leave, at	1 41	"	14,100
To the owners of limestone quarries for quarry-leave, at . .	13⅓	"	1,333
To capitalists for the use of money, interest, &c., at . . .	1 50	"	15,000
To railroad and canal companies, clear profits over and above expenses, for carrying coal to works, at	3 78	"	37,800
To storekeepers and others, for merchandise, &c., oil, brass, fire-brick, &c., at	2 39½	"	23,917
Cost at works, at	$49 00	"	$490,000
Transportation to market, say at	1 00	"	10,000
Drayage and hauling, at	50	"	5,000
Storage and other expenses, at	50	"	5,000
Commission for selling and guarantee, at 5 per cent., ...	2 75	"	27,500
	$53 75	"	$537,500
Cr.			
By sales at market price, at	55 00	"	550,000
Profit to manufacturer, at	$1 25	"	$12,500

CLARION COUNTY, formed in 1839 of parts of Venango and Armstrong. Its formations lie in the lower coal measures, the carbonate iron-ores of those measures occurring frequently throughout the county. This ore belongs to the lower coal measures of the bituminous series of Western Pennsylvania, and is called limestone or buhrstone ore. It is a mixture of peroxide and proto-carbonate of iron, the latter predominating except near the outcrop. It forms a regular wide-spread stratum below the Fossiliferous Limestone, underlying a wide area in the Fifth and Sixth coal basins or a large part of Armstrong, Venango, Clarion, Mercer, Butler, and Beaver counties. In the shales of the lower coal measures a nodular carbonate ore occurs, sometimes known as "Clarion ore," 6 to 14 inches thick, in shale overlaid by clays containing ore balls. But the deposits are not regular. Bog ore is also frequent in Clarion and Venango counties.

In 1840 there were 25 charcoal-furnaces, with a yearly product of " 50,000 to 55,000 tons of pig iron." The earliest works was the Shippensville furnace, built in 1832. The iron was boated to Pittsburg, on the Clarion and Allegheny rivers.

In 1849 one hot-blast charcoal-furnace made 1280 tons, and 22 of the 28 existing cold-blast furnaces actually made 23,340 tons of No. 3 iron. The height of these furnaces was 32 feet and the boshes about 8 feet, the majority having only one tuyere. The Shippensville forge made 50 tons of bar iron.

In 1856 there were 16 charcoal-furnaces, with a product of 18,933 tons.

In 1873 there was only 1 charcoal-furnace left, which made 2048 tons, but there were 2 coke-furnaces, 1 built in 1859, the other (the old Sligo) in 1845, for charcoal, and now being rebuilt for coke. The one in operation made, in 1873, 5565 tons of pig iron.

In the history of this county substantial furnaces arise and disappear like the visions of a dream; the contemplation of such changes dissipates the idea of permanence in a given locality, so far as pig iron is concerned. The ores were too lean to withstand the competition of those from Lake Superior.

CLEARFIELD COUNTY, formed in 1804 of parts of Lycoming and Northumberland. Its formations immediately underlie the coal measures which appear along the steep hillsides, and enter the tops of the easternmost hills at Karthaus. Samuel Boyd detected coal on Clearfield creek in 1785, and located a warrant on lands bought of the Indians, 3 miles above the town of Clearfield or Chincleclamoose. His son William, in 1804, sent down the first ark-load of coal to Columbia. In 1813, Peter Karthaus opened a mine at the mouth of Little Moshannon creek and shipped coal, in 1828, by ark, to Port Deposit, and thence to Philadelphia and Baltimore, selling it at 33 cents per bushel. In the first basin at Phillipsburg, Osceola, and on the Moshannon, a 5-foot, a 4½-foot, and a 3½-foot vein, and a 6-foot vein at Karthaus are now worked, and in the Second basin at Curwensville a 3½-foot vein is worked, less thick yet workable veins being found at Clearfield and in the third basin in the north-western part of the county. In 1874 the shipment of coal from the county was 658,315 net tons.

The only iron-works in this county has been the furnace built in 1820 by Peter Karthaus, of Baltimore, on the West Branch of the Susquehanna. It was intended to use the argillaceous carbonate ores of the local coal measures, developed there in a nodular strata, and in a stratum of compact ore, averaging about 39 per cent. of iron. Peter Karthaus conducted the furnace successfully for some years. In 1828 Karthaus sent 100 tons of castings and pig metal down the Susquehanna to Harrisburg. In 1836 the property was sold to a company. Professor Walter Johnson stated, in 1838, that the results of the furnace had shown that one ton of pig iron required three tons of raw ore, three and one-half tons of raw coal, and one ton of limestone.

Johnson estimated the cost in 1838 as follows:—

Ore costs to mine $1.75 per ton—3 tons, $5 25
Coal costs to mine 73 cents per ton—3½
   tons, ... 1 45
Limestone costs to mine $1.12½, . . 1 12½
Hauling 7½ tons at $38\frac{6}{10}$ cents per ton, 2 89½
Furnace labor, 13 hands at $1.40, on 9
   tons per day, ... 2 00
General expense at works and furnace, . 1 00

Furnace makes, say 63 tons per week, at $14 72 per ton.

The furnace was stopped in 1840, and has since done nothing. Deficient transportation was the immediate cause of stoppage, for their unwieldy arks are said to have left as much iron at the bottom of the Susquehanna as they got down for sale. The furnace was rebuilt in 1835 or 1836, and then made *coke iron*, being one of the first works in the State to produce it. Its capacity was then said to be one hundred tons a week. Several hundred tons of coke pig were actually made, but were unsalable, for want of care in selection of the ore had made the iron white and cold-short.

It is, however, a wonder that iron was made at all, for in 1838 the stack (45 feet high and 13 feet at the bosh) worked with 3 tuyeres and cold blast conducted from 2 blowing-cylinders (62-inch diameter by 72-inch stroke) through a plank box and logs dug out into semi-cylindrical sections, two of which were bound together by iron hoops to make the pipe. One Calder hot-blast oven was then in course of construction, but the coke iron had been made in a furnace of that size *with cold blast!*

CLINTON COUNTY, erected in 1829 from parts of Lycoming and Clinton. The county includes outcrops of all the measures, from the Upper Silurian limestone of (II.) Nittany valley to the coal formation west of the Allegheny ridge. In the hills on the Tangascootac and Queen's Run creek a small division of the First basin contains three workable coal veins. The veins on the Tangascootac were worked somewhat for the Farrandsville works. Fire-clay of excellent quality occurs with the coal.

The only important ore in this county is that of the Vergent (Devonian) strata. It crops out in a continuous range through parts of Lycoming, Clinton, and Tioga counties, but is best developed at Larry's creek, where the principal bed is 3 feet thick. It resembles Cleveland ironstone. Near Farrandsville there occurs in the lower red shale a nodular, compact, red hematite with about 49 per cent. iron, but so irregular and silicious that it was abandoned by the old furnace company.

Very little iron has been made in the county. One charcoal-furnace (the Washington) was built in 1809, and is still at work; but the history of affairs is somewhat like that of Clearfield. In 1831–2 William P. Farrand, of Philadelphia, began to mine coal, and built a furnace and nail-works at Farrandsville, using a steamboat to tow lime up and coal down the Susquehanna. In 1835 a nail-mill, making 10 tons a day, and a rolling-mill were added, and another furnace begun. At this time Mr. Farrand devoted himself exclusively to his railroad, as he was the originator and engineer of the Elmira and Williamsport Railroad, removed to Williamsport in 1833, and expended his resources in finishing the road to Ralston, in 1837.

The unfavorable location for transportation, and the irregularity of the Farrandsville ore and the extensive plans of the projectors proved the ruin of the works, though not till $700,000 of Boston capital had been sunk. These works were built expressly for using coke, and made coke iron in 1837, but they brought their ore 100 miles from Bloomsburg and 23 miles from Larry's creek, because they could not use their own ore. The furnace was 54 feet high, with 17-foot boshes, afterwards reduced to 13 feet. In 1839 the furnace made 50 tons of iron a week, with the following materials per ton of iron:—Coke, 2.9 tons; ore, 2.98 tons; limestone, 2 tons. Being unsuccessful with coke it used charcoal after September, 1839.

In 1856 1 charcoal-furnace and 1 forge made, respectively, 1200 tons of pig and 350 tons of bar iron.

In 1873 1 charcoal-furnace made 1150 tons of pig iron, and 1 forge made 1500 tons of blooms.

COLUMBIA COUNTY, formed in 1813 of part of Northumberland. The county is a sea of lines of elevation and depression, which bring to view all the measures from the Medina sandstones (IV.) to the conglomerate under the anthracite. At Danville, and along Montour ridge as far east as Bloomsburg, a valuable vein of brownish-red fossil ore crops out in great development, with a double outcrop to each band, owing to the top of the anticlinal ridge having been denuded.

The ore is the soft, calcareous fossil ore of the shales of the Clinton series previously described in Bedford and Blair counties. It reaches, in numerous lines of outcrop, from Western New York to Cumberland Gap, in Tennessee. It is accompanied by the hard ore in the iron sandstone 30 to 40 feet above it. The hard ore has an average thickness of 14 to 18 inches, and the soft ore 16 to 18 inches, the fossiliferous iron limestone bed being converted into workable ore about 32 yards to the dip, on an average. The total quantity of ore above water level in Montour's Ridge is estimated by Rogers at 3,672,000 tons; before so much is won the soft ore will be totally exhausted, but this estimate is too low. (See Montour.)

In 1842 there were the 2 furnaces of the Montour Iron-works, built in 1840 by Colonel Chambers, then "the most complete works in the United States, and capable of making 10,000 tons per annum;" the Columbia furnace, built in 1839, and run by J. P. & I. Groves, and the Danville, built for charcoal in 1838 and altered in 1839 to anthracite by Biddle, Chambers & Co., and afterwards bought by the Montour Iron Company. These 4 furnaces were among the very first in the country to use anthracite, as will be seen below. In 1845 the Pennsylvania Iron-works were built by the Montour Iron Company, which failed, and furnaces and mills are consolidated under the present name. The Irondale furnace (14 feet bosh, 35 feet high, built 1844) used these ores with an average yield of 56 per cent. With three 3¾-inch tuyeres and a blast of 2½ pounds, it made an average of 8100 tons, but on reduction to 12-foot bosh made in 1857 about 6000 tons.

In 1856 3 charcoal-furnaces made 2690 tons, 5 anthracite-furnaces made 17,000 tons of pig iron, and 1 forge produced 125 tons of blooms.

In 1873 there were 3 anthracite-furnaces, with a product of 19,868 tons of pig iron; 1 rolling-mill, making 1000 tons, and 1 forge, which made 462 tons of blooms.

In 1850 Columbia lost its principal iron district by its separation as Montour county, which see for its later history.

CUMBERLAND COUNTY, formed in 1750 of part of Lancaster. The formations of the county include the primal sandstone, the great Lower Silurian limestone formation, and the slates and sand rocks covering it to the west.

The county contains the richest body of hematite ore in the State, reaching over 12 miles, from Mount Holly up the Yellow Breeches creek. The ore contains a good deal of manganese, which aids in making blooms, but in puddling makes iron of a hard and steely character. From a furnace using this ore I have seen specimens of white iron, equaling spiegel iron as to manganese, but containing too much phosphorus for use in making steel.

The South mountain consists largely of hard white

sandstone, at or near the contact of which with the limestone on its northern flank brown hematite is most extensively mined on a deposit almost continuous from Mont Alto to Papertown. The ore is derived from a belt of slate between the primal and calciferous sandstones, and includes wash-ore and solid ore deposits of varying thickness, and for the greater part of cold-short quality. It is mixed at Boiling Springs (Ahl's furnace) with 25 per cent. of magnetic or limestone ore, and requires 130 to 140 bushels charcoal per ton of iron. At Big Pond, Pine Grove, and several other points, it can be used unmixed. It has averaged for many years 2½ tons to the ton of iron. The quantity is practically unlimited, and further extensive deposits are found in pockets and strips all over the limestone formation of the valley.

Ebeling, in 1797, states that there were 5 forges in the county—Carlisle, Chambersburg, Middletown, Eges', and Mount Pleasant forge, built in 1783. Pine Grove furnace was built in 1770, ran till recently, and had, in 1870, the last extant specimens of the old single-acting wooden blowing-tubs. Holly furnace was built in 1795 and Cumberland furnace in 1794: both were abandoned about 1854 with Cumberland forge, all for want of charcoal.

At Middlesex, during the Revolution, 2 wrought-iron cannon were made by William Denning; they were built of long segmental bars, which broke joint 4 times, welded and carefully hooped. One of these was taken by the British at Brandywine. The British Government offered a reward and annuity to any one who would make the guns for them, but Denning did not do it. (Hazard.)

The Fairview Works, now the Harrisburg Nail-works, were built in 1831, and used coal from Clearfield county, brought down in arks, to heat their blooms. In 1832 their product was four to six tons per day, which was sent to Philadelphia, and they were preparing to roll sheet iron and use *anthracite coal to heat it*. They have always used an excellent water-power at the mouth of Conedogwinit creek.

In 1840 the county contained 8 charcoal-furnaces and 5 forges.

In 1856 there were 3 charcoal-furnaces, producing 1400 tons of pig metal, and 4 forges making 1104 tons of blooms. The Fairview Works did not run between 1849 and 1857.

In 1873 there were 5 charcoal-furnaces, with a product of 5854 tons of pig; one rolling-mill, which made 6241 tons, and 2 forges, which turned out 1943 tons of blooms.

DAUPHIN COUNTY, formed in 1785 of part of Lancaster. The county includes all formations, from the Lower Silurian limestone upward to the coal, and contains two anthracite coal basins, which are the two tongues into which the Southern anthracite basin splits toward the west. It contains comparatively little iron-ore, mainly brown hematite, in unimportant deposits. In Rausch Gap, in the northern tongue, a *black-band* vein 12 inches thick was mined (over one of the coal seams), which was discovered 1845, and regarded as highly important. The coal is mainly used for household purposes; for furnaces Schuylkill and Lehigh coals are used, and Clearfield bituminous coals for the mills.

In 1797 there was in the county 1 furnace, belonging to Peter Grubb, which supplied a forge in Chester county. Grubb had another forge in the Blue Hills, on the Swatara, and all were in operation.

In 1856 the county had 1 charcoal-furnace, the

Manada, built in 1837 by E. B. & C. B. Grubb, which made 1598 tons of pig iron, in 1855, from Cornwall and Chestnut Hill ore; 6 anthracite-furnaces, the earliest that of Governor Porter, built in 1845, which made 16,648 tons of pig iron; 2 forges, making 667 tons of blooms, and 1 rolling-mill, the Central (the Harrisburg idle since 1853), which made 1400 tons of boiler-plate out of blooms.

In 1873 there were 11 anthracite-furnaces, with a product of 45,870 tons; 1 charcoal-furnace, not reporting; 4 rolling-mills, which made 10,803 tons of boiler-plate and nails; 1 forge, making 950 tons of blooms; 2 rail-mills, with a product of 37,229 tons, one of which is the Lochiel, and the other the Pennsylvania Steel-works, at Baldwin. The New York market is largely supplied with Harrisburg boiler-plate. All the mills are in the immediate vicinity of that city.

The Pennsylvania Steel-works were built, in 1865-6, with 2 five-ton vessels, and the rail-mill, in 1867-8, with 1 twenty-three-inch train, and gradually enlarged to its present size by the addition of a heavy forge in 1869 with a thirteen-ton hammer, a foundry, pattern-shop, &c. The blast-furnace belonging to the works went into operation in 1873, having been built in eleven months through a severe winter. It was the first in the country to make Bessemer iron out of mixed ores. Both ores and coal were selected by chemical analysis with entire success. In 1872 a second Bessemer plant was commenced on an improved plan of Mr. J. B. Pearse, but was suspended owing to the scarcity of pig iron being so great as to necessitate the erection of a furnace. In 1873 the works made 19,054 tons of rails out of 6 and 7 furnaces, on single turn, and 2 large Siemens' furnaces were built in that year, to increase the capacity of the mill. A second blast-furnace was in course of erection in 1875 and also a blooming-mill, the latter contemplated in 1873.

To the Pennsylvania Steel Company and its managers credit is due for the labor of making Bessemer steel manufacture a *commercial success* in this country, and for having first, in 1869, led the way in forming American *steel metallurgy* by the systematic use of chemical analysis, till then entirely neglected by the experimental works at Wyandotte and Troy. At Wyandotte steel was first made in the fall of 1864, and at Troy in a 2½-ton vessel, February 16th, 1865. The Wyandotte works were bought of the Kelley Pneumatic Company by E. B. Ward, and abandoned 1869, the Kelley and Bessemer interests having been united in 1866. The Troy vessel made most of the experimental steel, for the Troy 5-ton vessel plant, completed in 1867, lay idle till it was started by Mr. Z. S. Durfee, in the fall of 1868, and was burnt soon after. The works were rebuilt and started again January 12th, 1870, by Mr. A. L. Holley. At Troy, Winslow, Griswold & Holley had experimented with pig irons for Bessemer use, noting their value by their blowing and mechanical properties; but the Troy experience was no guide to the Pennsylvania Steel Company, and had it not been for the attention directed there to the chemical constitution of American irons, the Bessemer process would hardly now be successful. The Pennsylvania works were built, by a company of which Mr. S. M. Felton was and is president, under the auspices of the Pennsylvania Railroad, and that road, through Mr. J. Edgar Thomson, afforded the support and assistance necessary for the introduction of steel rails. Mr. J. H. Linville was chief engineer of the Pennsylvania Steel-works, and used the Troy plans as a basis for his erection. Mr. Holley was the first manager, became consulting engineer of the company in the summer of 1868, severing connection with it at the end of 1868, being succeeded by H. S. Nourse and J. B. Pearse, the latter having charge of manufacture. In the fall of 1869 Mr. Pearse took charge as general manager of the company, Mr. Nourse remaining as superintendent. Mr. Nourse resigned 1873, Mr. Pearse early in 1874, and Mr. L. S. Bent then took charge. In 1867 the Pennsylvania Steel Company began the regular manufacture of steel ingots, being the first to do so on a manufacturing scale. Cambria rolled the early product made at Harrisburg (Cambria Steel-works not starting till July 10th, 1871), and in 1868 the latter company rolled its own product. When the Harrisburg works started, 3 blows per turn of 12 hours was a full day's work; in 1868 they produced 8 blows per half day, at that time the best practice in the world. In 1868 the McKenzie cupola, with annular air-slot tuyere, melted 14 tons of iron per day—could not be coaxed to melt more. In 1869, one had been designed at Harrisburg, by Mr. Pearse, that melted regularly 40 to 60 tons per day. It had 6 elliptical tuyeres (total area, say 190 square inches) put in at first 38 then 42 inches above the bottom, with a blast of about three-quarters of a pound to the square inch. This form of cupola is now used in all American steel-works. In 1872 it was improved simultaneously at Harrisburg and Johnstown by the addition of a slag-tapping hole, so that it now melts 105 to 130 tons per half day easily, and can, if desired, run 18 to 24 hours at that rate. By later improvements and the successful invention of the cast-iron runner (Pearse), it may be run longer, even several days, if the bottom be water-cooled.

This vast improvement in smelting capacity stimulated improvement of the converting vessels, and in 1869 the best form of converter-bottom (Holley's) was introduced at Troy, having been worked out during trials of a joint design of Holley and Pearse. This has also been adopted at nearly all the works in this country. In 1870 it was introduced at Harrisburg, and by its use, in connection with the improved cupolas, a product of 32 blows (1,363,406 pounds of steel) was made in 22 hours, at that time something unheard of,—the product of the European works being 12 blows in 24 hours. The Johnstown works made 133 heats in one week, in February, 1872. At the end of 1872 the Harrisburg works produced 150 blows in a week, and the Johnstown, early in 1873, made 154 blows in a week. In 1873 the Harrisburg works made in a week 180 blows, yielding 890 tons of ingots. Mr. A. L. Holley states that in January, 1874, the Cambria works made 189 blows with 956 tons of ingots; while in February the Troy works made 50 blows and 267 tons of ingots in 24 hours, and in April 195 blows and 972 tons of ingots in a week. The largest product of these three works up to date have been (in gross tons):—Harrisburg, 281 tons per day, 1291 tons per week, 5455 per month; Cambria, 297 tons per day, 1475 tons per week, 6051 per month; Troy, regularly, 1300 tons per week, 5498 tons in the heaviest month,—the greatest product yet reached is that at North Chicago, of 330 gross tons per day, 1583 per week, and 6457 per month.

The unbroken success of the Pennsylvania Steel Company—a very rare thing for a new works in this country—was partly due to the use of a hammer for blooming the ingots, which, for experimental work, is the best tool; though it will not produce as much as a blooming-mill, it will turn out a far sounder product when the steel is bad. Between hammering (13-ton hammer) at Harrisburg and blooming at Cambria there was, in 1873, not more than eighty cents difference per ton, the hammer using old furnaces and the mill Siemen's furnaces. But the hammer, when it started, did as much as a rail train did, and bloomed nearly 90 tons of ingots in 24 hours, with three sets of men. The Harrisburg works, making, as they did, the first rails on order, were obliged to bear the brunt of English efforts to retain the trade, and the fluctuation of prices resulting from these efforts and from home competition is shown by the following table, prepared by Mr. Charles S. Hinchman :—

YEAR.	January.	February.	March.	April.	May.	June.	July.	August.	September.	October.	November.	December.	Yearly Average.
1868, ...	165	167½	174	172	165	162½	150	150	150	150	148	147½	158½
1869, ...	145	143¼	135	134	130¼	128	130	130	130	130½	130¼	120	132¼
1870, ...	110	110	108½	107	106	109¼	110	110	108¾	101½	102½	98	106¾
1871, ...	95	96	106	95	103	104	103¾	104	106	105¾	105¼	106½	102½
1872, ...	104½	104	104¼	111½	110	113	114½	115¼	114	113½	118	120¾	112
1873, ...	121	116	122½	120¼	120	121¾	121¾	121¾	118	120	120	120	120½
1874, ...	117½	117½	115	98¾	98½	96¼	91	89¼	85	87¾	93	78	97¼
1875, ...	95	83½	78¾	80¾	77½	73¾	74½	76½	76½	73½	72	72¼	78
1876, ...	69¼	69	65¼	62	61¼	63	. . .	. . .	. . .	. . .	. . .	. . .	65*

* Average for six months. Quotations are all in dollars, U. S. currency.

DELAWARE COUNTY, formed in 1789 of part of Chester. The formations are entirely primary, with beds of serpentine. No iron-ore is found.

The iron industry never took root in this county. Ore was too scarce and wood too valuable. The only record remaining is that in 1830 there were in the county 4 rolling and slitting mills, with a product of 300 tons of sheet, 500 tons of hoop and rod iron, and 600 tons of nails. These all died a natural death before 1840.

ERIE COUNTY, formed in 1800 of part of Allegheny. Its formations are the sandstones, shales, and slates underlying the coal measures. They contain some deposits of ore, which have not proved valuable. Natural gas occurs at Erie in limited quantity.

In 1840 a charcoal blast-furnace was supplied from a deposit of surface ore within seven miles of Erie. The Lake Superior ores meet coal at this point, and in 1869 the Erie furnace was built for raw coal. In 1873 one furnace made 5373 tons with raw coal, and 1 rolling-mill 3812 tons. A furnace of large size is projected at Corry. In 1874 the Erie furnace was altered to a charcoal-furnace, 10-foot bosh, 51 feet high. With lean ores 112 bushels were required, but rich ores, such as Jackson, are smelted with 80 to 90 bushels to the ton. Natural gas was tried at the furnace, allowing it to blow in by its own pressure through a ⅜-inch pipe inserted in the tuyere. No special advantage was attained.

FAYETTE COUNTY, formed in 1783 of part of Westmoreland. It belongs wholly in the bituminous coal formation, and contains vast quantities of the finest coal of the Second basin in the Ligonier valley, and of the Connellsville trough, with the Pittsburg bed and seams above it, and considerable outcrops of calcareous carbonate ore near the bases of Laurel Hill and Chestnut Ridge.

The ore is that of the red shales of the Umbral series of Rogers, and is mined close under the (Seral) conglomerate in many parts of the State. At Hopewell a bed in fire-clay contains 2½ feet of ore in flattened balls, and the same ore has been worked near Pittston, at Kingston Hollow, near Wilkesbarre, at Ralston, at Blossburg, and extensively in South-western Pennsylvania. It varies from 8 to 84 inches in all (Kingston Gap). In Fayette county, in about 100 feet of shales (XI.), under the conglomerate, 5 carbonate ore-beds occur,—a lean ore 30 inches thick; the " Big Bottom" 18-inch solid ore, in blue slate; the "Flag" 8 to 12 inches thick, but thinning out at 30 to 40 yards in; an unnamed bed 6 to 10 inches, a foot above which is the Honeycomb ore 5 to 12 inches thick. The veins are overlaid by fire-clay and contain, raw, 35.6 to 37.6 per cent. of iron, and 10.8 to 13.8 per cent. of silica. Other coal-beds are mined locally, but the Pittsburg bed supplies coal at Connellsville and other points on the Youghiogheny which can be mined, coked, and sold in the cars for $1.37 per net ton. About 1 to 4 feet below the Pittsburg bed a 30 per cent. calcareous iron-ore has recently been discovered, of an average thickness of 12 to 16 inches where it is found. Eight to 12 feet below the Pittsburg bed 3 local beds of high quality are mined for Fairchance furnace.

Ebeling states that in 1797 there were 2 furnaces and 2 forges that produced the best iron. These were the Fairchance furnace and forge and the Union furnace.

In this county *the first furnaces west of the Alleghenies* were built, and there are 3 which claim precedence, viz., Mary Ann, built 1777 or 1784, by Mr. Oliphant, Sr., in Greene county, 30 miles from Uniontown (Lesley); Turnbull & Marmie's furnace, on Jacob's creek, blown in in 1790, and the Union furnace, on Dunbar creek, built in 1791 by Meason, Gibson, and Moses Dillon. Turnbull & Marmie cast cannon-balls, in 1791, for the defense of Pittsburg, and in 1793 for the expedition of General Wayne against the Indians. There is a romantic legend connected with Marmie. He was passionately fond of hunting; failed on Jacob's creek and returned to France. He started another furnace there, but was again unsuccessful and became deranged. Going to the furnace-mouth, he threw his hounds in first and then jumped in himself.

The date of the Mary Ann furnace is very doubtful, and it seems almost certain that the Jacob's creek was the first furnace in Western Pennsylvania (*vide* Jacob's furnace, Westmoreland county). The first wrought iron however, was made by John Hayden, who discovered the nodular ore in 1790. William Turnbull, of Philadelphia, and Peter Marmie were engaged in trade at Fort Pitt, the site of which they claimed to have bought; in 1790, they with John Holkar, consul-general of France, began the "Alliance Iron-works," furnace, forge, &c., at the mouth of Jacob's creek, fifteen miles below Connellsville. The records of Westmoreland county, March sessions, 1791, fix these facts, and the dissolution of partnership was advertised in Pittsburg, August 26th, 1793. Marmie then ran the works till his failure in 1795, perhaps, for Francis Bryan & Co. advertise "a quantity of sugar-kettles and bar iron for sale, mouth of Jacob's creek, February 2d, 1795."

In the spring of 1789 John Hayden came from the ore region of New Jersey and settled near the present

Fairchance Iron-works. In looking for limestone, he gathered "blue lump" ore from a creek bed which would not slake when calcined, and was very heavy. He then made of it, as he said, "a piece of iron about as big as a harrow-tooth," using a smith's forge. Coming east to secure money, he was joined by John Nicholson, of Philadelphia, then State comptroller. They took up tracts of land at the base of Laurel Hill, and about 1792 Hayden built the Fairfield furnace, 7 miles south of Uniontown. He failed when Nicholson defaulted, and F. H. Oliphant, Sr., bought the property.

The Union furnace, afterward Youghiogheny, then Dunbar, was originally a small furnace built by Isaac Meason, a deputy surveyor, on Dunbar creek, 3 miles south of Connellsville, on part of the lands of Christopher Gist (the guide of Washington), who had here planted, in 1752, the first permanent English settlement west of the Alleghenies. In 1793 he built a large furnace on the same site, admitting Moses Dillon to a sixth interest in 1793. The firm was Meason, Dillon & Co., and the "American Pioneer" states John Gibson as one of the firm. They advertised castings in 1794 "at the reduced price of £35 sterling ($93.10) per ton." This furnace was the most successful in the region, and sold its kettles, &c. in the West for Spanish dollars at a great profit. At a later period, with greater competition, it was necessary to trade, and Mr. E. C. Pechin, of Dunbar, says one old ironmaster told him he had carried on business for three years seeing only $10 in money. Isaac Meason bought out Dillon and built a second furnace on Morent's creek, at the base of Chestnut Ridge, and a third on Dunbar creek, a few miles above the first. He was the most successful ironmaster of his day in Western Pennsylvania, and in 1804 he filled the first order for large-sized sugar-kettles for sugar plantations then being laid out near New Orleans. Dillon went to Ohio, and Gibson, if he was an iron-master at all, has left no record.

The great western demand, which General Benner, for a time, partially supplied, caused this early activity in Fayette. Charcoal-furnaces soon became too small, and experiments with coke began. It seems certain that the *first coke iron made in the State* was produced by F. H. Oliphant, of Fayette, in 1836, who sent samples, at the time, to the Franklin Institute, in Philadelphia; but he did not continue to make it, as charcoal iron was more valuable. Karthaus also made coke pig in 1836, and the Farrandsville furnace in 1837. Would they had all been successful!

In 1840 there were 9 charcoal-furnaces in the county, making 1800 tons of pig iron, and 3 forges, with a product of 703 tons of bar iron.

In 1856 there were 4 charcoal-furnaces, the Spring Hill—fourth on the same site, Fairchance, Union, and Redstone, which produced 2410 tons of pig iron, and 1 forge, with a product of 600 tons of bar iron. There were then, too, 16 abandoned charcoal-furnaces in the county which had been built between 1805 and 1835. The Spring Hill and the Union furnaces had, in 1856, the same dimensions, 9-foot bosh, 35 feet in height, 2 feet at mouth, and were blown respectively through one 2½-inch and two 3½-inch tuyeres with warm blast, producing, respectively, 246 and 964 tons each in 28 and 33 weeks. This difference is a startling one, but the comparison is fair and shows how money is made.

In 1873 there were 1 charcoal-furnace (Spring Hill, built 1805), 2 coke-furnaces, with a product of 15,313 tons,—one of them, Oliphant's, rebuilt, in 1871, for coke; the other, the Dunbar, built in 1870,—and 1 rolling-mill, which made 244 tons of bar iron.

FRANKLIN COUNTY, formed in 1784 of part of Cumberland. Its formations include the South mountain primal rocks and the Lower Silurian limestone formation of the Great Valley, bounded to the west by the dark Matinal shales and slates (III.), and to the westward the measures are broken by axes of elevation, exposing the measures up to the olive slates (VIII.) of the Hamilton series in the hills of the "Little Cove." The limestone series has a development equal to that of Cumberland county, and to that description of the iron-ore at the base of the South mountain nothing need be added; but long, narrow limestone basins carrying brown hematite alternate with the Matinal slates, the longest reaching from the Maryland line through Loudon Gap to the head of Path valley. In the Little Cove the Clinton series carries its fossil ore with the hard ore of the Iron-sandstone, both worked by the Warren furnace (1835, now abandoned), 16 miles from Millstone Point, on the Chesapeake and Ohio canal. The same ore crops out along the west base of the North mountain, from Fannetsburg to Loudon, and was used by the Carrick cold-blast furnace (1828) still running. The easternmost furnaces used the brown hematites, which are mostly cold-short.

This county contained the Mount Pleasant forge, stated, by Schöpf, to have been in operation in 1783. Mount Pleasant furnace, in Path valley, was built, in 1783, by William, Benjamin, and George Chambers, sons of Benjamin Chambers, Sr. The Loudon furnace and forge were built, about 1790, by Colonel James Chambers, an elder brother of the above gentlemen. These furnaces did their work, and were abandoned, respectively, in 1843 and 1840. They lay on the early highway to the West, and their situation secured a large trade. Nails were so scarce there that, in 1785, Benjamin Chambers, Sr.'s house was *burned by an incendiary for the nails it contained!*

In 1829 there were in the county 5 charcoal-furnaces and 6 forges; production not stated. (Hazard.)

In 1856 there were 6 charcoal-furnaces (including the Caledonia), with a product of 3800 tons of pig iron; 6 forges, which made 600 tons of blooms and bars, and 1 rolling-mill (Mont Alto, built 1832), which made 500 tons of bar iron.

In 1873 there were 5 charcoal-furnaces, which made 6048 tons of pig iron, and 1 forge (the old Mont Alto mill), which made 1386 tons of blooms.

In 1875 the Carrick, Franklin, and Mont Alto charcoal-furnaces still existed, the latter with a forge of 7 fires, a refinery, and a Nasmyth hammer.

HUNTINGDON COUNTY, formed in 1787 of part of Bedford. It includes all the secondary formations, Lower and Upper Silurian, Devonian, and carboniferous, and in the south-western corner, at Broad Top, contains part of that isolated coal-field.

The Lower Silurian limestone (II.) appears in Kichicoquillas valley and Sinking valley, thence broadening out northward over Warrior's Mark, and Franklin townships. These limestones contain vast deposits of brown hematite pipe, argillaceous, or sandy ore, according to composition of the original rock stratum from which the ore is derived, and whose place, though in distorted positions, the ore yet fills. The old bank of the Pennsylvania furnace on Spruce creek, illustrated below, is the finest exhibition of this ore accessible to study. Professor Lesley, in a report on the lands of Lyon,

Short & Co., occupying nearly all Warrior's Mark, and
Franklin townships, separates four ranges of brown
hematite ore, the Pennington, belonging to the older
strata and corresponding to the Bloomfield ore of Blair,
the Warrior's Mark, and Lovetown range of a higher
geological horizon than the Pennington, the Dry Hollow range, with quite sandy ore, and the Cale Hollow
(pipe-ore) and Spruce creek range, coalescing north of
Huntingdon furnace. The Spruce creek range has been
longest and most successfully worked; 35 feet of its
wash ore paying for stripping off 65 to 75 feet of clays
above it. In order to save money it has been mostly
worked by "shallow diggings and ground-hogging"
methods, but now needs systematic exploration and will
most amply repay it. The limestone valley, from Half
Moon in Centre to Morrison's Cove in Blair, contains
probably the greatest brown hematite ore deposits in
the State.

In the Medina sandstone appearing on Tuscarora,
Shade, Blacklog, Jack's, and Stone mountain, unimportant outcrops of ore are found on the last two.

The Clinton shales appear with their double-banded
fossil ore in all the mountain ranges of the county.
The bands, however, are frequently rather too thin to
be productive. It has been principally worked along
the Great Aughwick valley at Orbisonia (where it is
now largely mined by the Rockhill Coal and Iron Company), at Mount Union (6 tons to 1 of metal), and other
points, and on the broad tract of shales and slate north
of Warrior's Ridge, at Greenwood, at Yellow creek in
Hopewell, and elsewhere. The Lewistown or Middle
Juniata valley has numerous outcrops on its anticlinals
and along the south flank of Jack's mountain. At
Middleburg the block ore was 7 feet thick and good,

elsewhere it is rather silicious. It now supports 2 anthracite-furnaces (Glamorgan) at Lewistown.

Beside these the Umbral red shales (XI.), which bear ore in other parts of the State, appear in Trough Creek valley and around Broad Top mountain. Their ore was mined at Hopewell and was mined for the old Trough Creek furnace.

For sixty years the ore-bank sketched below has supplied the Pennsylvania cold-blast charcoal-furnace, with ore out of which 50,000 tons of pig had been made up to 1874. The furnace was originally (1813) $8\frac{1}{2}$-foot bosh, 35 feet high, and one $2\frac{1}{2}$-inch tuyere, now $9\frac{1}{2}$ feet, 43 feet, and two tuyeres, 4-foot tunnel-head, bosh angle 68°, and hearth $5\frac{1}{2}$ feet deep by 48 inches diameter at top and 30 inches at bottom, a Player oven with 6 rows of pipes has lately been added. The sandy ores have been rejected and the remainder worked in forges into blooms for boiler-plate, the quality of which, as stated under Centre county, has been surpassingly good. The brown hematites of all the Lower Silurian limestone valleys closely resemble each other, yet vary largely in the percentage of phosphorus; that element seems to increase the lower the place of the ore in the series. These hematites contain 0.06 to 0.22 per cent. phosphorus and 44.77 to 58.19 per cent. of iron in the raw ore; the average of Pennsylvania bank is 0.065 phosphorus and 57.8 per cent. of iron.

The ore-bank is not only an old but a representative one, both to the geologist and metallurgist, and the sketches form a complete representation of a brown hematite wash ore-bank as now worked. Fig. 1 is the map of the workings, showing a plan of the buildings, &c. The "settling pond" is not shown, but is on a

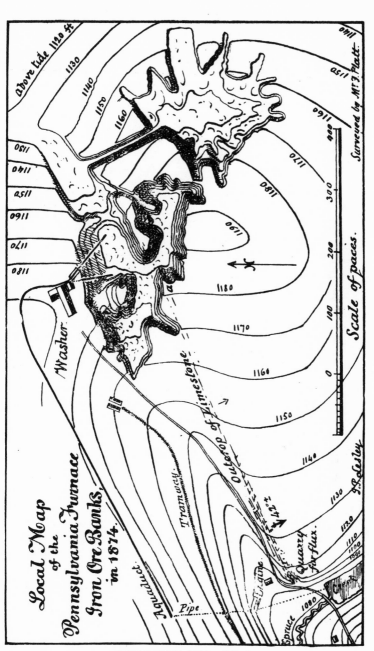

PENNSYLVANIA BANK.—FIG. I.

level with the bottom of the cutting and in a hollow to the north-east.

Fig. 2 shows the engine-house, from which a 12-inch

PENNSYLVANIA BANK.—FIG. 2.

pipe rises sharply 110 feet up to the aqueduct, which leads the water 2000 feet along the ridge to the washer.

Fig. 3 represents the main ore-bank seen to the north-ward from the point *a*, fig. 1. The floor of the excavation is about 60 feet below the washer, and shafts sunk 30 to 35 feet deeper to the water level have proved other and even better deposits beneath. The amount "*in sight*," or exposed by cuts or shafts, in this bank is not less than 600,000 tons of prepared ore. In the limestone outcrop to the right, which lies at *a*, fig. 1, the "red ore" is worked, so to speak in place, over and between the strata of limestone.

Fig. 4 shows the south-east cutting, illustrating the position of the "wash ore." The bank has never been worked in the more solid ore at the bottom, owing to convenience of the western cutting. Most of the banks in the vicinity have been abandoned, when sunk to near the water level, after leaving the best ore in the floor.

Pennsylvania Furnace Ore Banks.

J P Lesley

PENNSYLVANIA BANK.—FIG. 3.

The books of the furnace show, as an average, 6 tons of wash ore to 1 ton of prepared ore; 2 tons 1 cwt. of ore to 1 ton of iron; and $2 per ton at the furnace represents the cost of prepared ore, including all expenses.

The ore-earth is loaded into cars, carrying 29½ cubic feet, drawn by horses 300 to 500 feet to the foot of the incline, and there lifted 37 feet on a grade of 14° by an engine with 12 inch 2 feet stroke, and a pair of 8-foot drums, to the level of the washer. The car-load is again dragged 150 feet and dumped into the washing-troughs, in which revolve three Archimedean screw-propellor shafts, 20, 26, and 26 feet long, respectively. The shafts are of decagonial timber, 15 inches in diameter, on the facets of which are screwed cast-iron blades. The ore travels 72 feet, and is dropped into two classifying-screens, the sand and mud being floated off to the set-tling-dam. The screens have one-quarter inch and one-twelfth inch meshes. The ore falls on sheet-iron trays, where the quartz is picked out. The washers are driven by an engine with 16-inch cylinder and 54-inch stroke. The water is supplied from Spruce creek by a Worth-ington pump, with 20-inch steam and 15-inch water cylinders. Six cubic yards of earth have been found to produce, on an average, 1 ton of washed ore, the dig-gers being paid 16 cents per car-load of 29.58 cubic feet, equaling 23.67 of solid earth. A cubic yard costs, there-fore, 18¼ cents, and a ton of ore $1.09. The ore delivered at the furnace costs $2, leaving 91 cents for carriage, washing, and delivery. The cost has at times been $2.25. (Report of Professor Lesley; J. W. Har-den described the mining.)

Ebeling, in 1797, mentions "two forges of J. Beal, at the foot of Tuscarora mountains."

Hazard's Register stated, in 1832, that in 1820 there

Wash Ore from bottom to top of stripping.

Wash Ore 40 to 50 feet deep

Pennsylvania Furnace, Old Banks, S.E. Cutting. Nov. 1873.—Lesley.

PENNSYLVANIA BANK.—FIG. 4.

were in Sinking valley 1 forge and 1 rolling and slitting mill.

In 1828 there were 8 furnaces, with a product of 6000 tons of pig iron, used by the forges of the county; 11 forges, making 1950 tons of bar iron and 1100 tons of blooms per annum; 1 slitting-mill at Tyrone, making yearly 150 tons nail-rods; and 1 steel-works, at Millington forge, which made steel of fine quality.

In 1832, "two young men, employed by the U. S. Secretary of the Treasury at $4 per day," ascertained that the annual product of the county was 795 tons of bar iron, 3372 tons of blooms, 7350 tons of pig iron, and 1600 tons of castings. (*Banner of the Constitution.*)

Before 1845 this county was the principal seat of the iron manufacture of the State, and in 1837 Harris gives the following census of the works:—On the Little Juniata there were 2 furnaces and 8 forges; on the Raystown branch, 2 furnaces and 3 forges; on Stone creek, 1 furnace (Pennsylvania) and 8 forges; on Shade creek, 2 furnaces; on Aughwick creek, 2 furnaces; on Warrior's Mark run, 1 furnace (Huntingdon); on Little Bald Eagle creek, 1 furnace; on Big Turtle creek, 1 furnace and 1 forge; on Piney creek, 1 furnace and 1 forge, and on Clove creek, 1 furnace. In all, 16 charcoal-furnaces, with an annual product of 13,750 tons of pig iron; 24 forges, with a product of 9309 tons of blooms and bars, and 1 rolling-mill. Of these, William Lyon & Co. owned the two Tyrone forges on the Little Juniata and the Bald Eagle furnace; Shorb, Stewart & Co. owned the Pennsylvania furnace and the three Coleraine forges on Spruce creek, all occupied on blooms for boiler-plate; G. & J. H. Schoenberger owned the Juniata forge, the Elizabeth forge on Spruce creek, the Huntingdon furnace on Warrior's Mark run; and the

Rebecca furnace on Clove creek belonged to Dr. Peter
Shoenberger. On Frankstown branch, the Etna furnace and forge and an unfinished (1837) furnace were
owned by H. S. Spang, and G. Hatfield & Co. were
building their mill.

In 1843 *Hazard's Gazette* stated that "the Bedford
furnace on Aughwick creek, near Shirleysburg, was
the first furnace built in Western Pennsylvania," and had
been long abandoned by its owners, Ridgeley & Cromwell, who sold the estate. On the site of its ruins Orbisonia was laid out. An advertisement in the *Pittsburg
Gazette* reads as follows:—

BEDFORD IRON-WORKS, situate and being in Huntingdon county
and Aughwick settlement. The furnace stands within 16 and the forge
within 12 miles of the intersection of the State road, at the foot of
Sideling Hill, are now in blast, and whereat any person may be supplied
with a neat and general assortment of Castings and Barr-Iron, the latter
warranted good; and to prevent imposition every barr in future will be
stamped with B. F. A generous price will be allowed for beef, pork, or
grain of every kind, in payment for the above.

Orders for either Castings or Barr-Iron, lodged with Mr. George
Wilds at the foot of Sideling Hill, Benjamin Burd, Esq., Littleton, or
Messrs. Scott & Kerr, merchants, at Strasburgh, will be duly attended to
by the public's humble servant.

THOMAS CROMWELL, *for Com.*

Bedford Iron-Works, Sept. 10, 1793.

N. B.—The small quantity of bad Iron that was made at the forge
last fall was occasioned by some mine which was raised at a new bank
opened towards the latter end of the blast.

The Huntingdon furnace, owned till 1843 by Judge
Gloninger of Lebanon, George Anshutz of Huntingdon,
Peter Shoenberger of Allegheny, and Martin Dubbs of
Philadelphia, was built in 1795–6, but was moved two
years afterward a mile eastward to a better location.
The business began with 15 acres, one horse, and one

pair of oxen, but succeeded so well under the management of Anshutz that in 1819 the company owned 40,000 acres. These works were gradually extended by building the Tyrone Works (upper and lower forges—1813–14—rolling and slitting mill, and nail factory) and the Bald Eagle furnace (1828) and a forge on Spruce creek. The Huntingdon furnace, with ore abundant, one to four miles from it, made in 1857 2106 tons of iron. It has recently been abandoned, and the interests of Lyon, Shorb & Co. and Shorb, Stewart & Co. having been consolidated, the Pennsylvania furnace only has been in blast.

In 1840 the county contained 20 furnaces, making 13,850 tons of pig iron, and 27 "bloomeries, forges, and rolling-mills," with a product of 14,093 tons. During the crisis of 1840–2 the works were obliged to suspend for want of money, and *orders* were issued. The practice was so abused that *orders became odious*, and the legislature forbade their issue. The men were then paid in "*long dollars*," or bars and pigs of iron, which they traded for the necessaries of life.

In 1856 there were at work 7 charcoal-furnaces, with a product of 7397 tons of pig iron, 7 forges, which made 3248 tons of blooms and bar iron, and 1 rolling-mill, with a product of 450 tons of bar iron.

In 1873 there were 4 charcoal-furnaces, which made 4180 tons of pig iron; 3 forges, with a product of 2100 tons of blooms. In 1874 there were 2 coke-furnaces.

All the pig iron was formerly made into blooms, which were shipped to Pittsburg. The Juniata iron was, in its later days as well as its earlier, celebrated throughout the country for its toughness and excellent qualities. Regarding the cost and amount of iron made in Centre, Huntingdon, and Mifflin counties, Mr. Mitchell, of Bellefonte, testified in 1828 before a committee of Congress. An abstract reads as follows:—

In the three counties there were made, in 1828, 8500 tons of pig iron and castings and 400 tons of bar iron.

There were as many forges in 1820 in Pennsylvania as now (1828), and 450 tons more bar iron was made in 1827 than in 1820.

6000 tons of pig are required for 4000 tons of bar iron, and at many works the men are required by contract to make one ton of bar out of one and a half tons of pig iron.

Charcoal to 1 ton of pig iron 220 bushels at 5 cents, and to 1 ton of bar iron made from pig 175 bushels at 6 cents.

Product: Mitchell estimated 100 tons yearly to each forge or finery fire, while Jackson of New Jersey estimated 25 to 30 tons for a bloomery fire.

Cost to Mitchell, at Bellefonte:—A ton of bar iron from pig cost $75, including pig at $26.67; all the bar in his section was made from pig.

Market: Two-thirds of product (blooms) goes to Pittsburg, with a freight of $25 to $30 per ton, and sells there at $100 to $115. To Baltimore the freight was $10, to Philadelphia $12, and the prices at those points $85 to $95 per ton. At the works bar iron sold for $100 when pig iron was $26.67 cents, at which price both were sold in 1828.

INDIANA COUNTY, formed in 1803 of parts of Westmoreland and Lycoming. The county lies entirely in the bituminous coal measures of the Third and Fourth basins.

The county was a wilderness till recently opened by the Bennett's Branch of the Allegheny Valley Railroad.

There were, however, in 1856, 2 charcoal-furnaces, built in 1842 and 1846, which made about 2455 tons in 1856. In 1874 no works remained.

LANCASTER COUNTY, formed in 1729 of part of Chester. The measures are Lower Silurian limestone (II.), occupying a wide belt through the centre of the county, from one side to the other, bounded to the south by older metamorphic primal strata (tale slate, mica slate, belts of serpentine), and to the north by the Mesozoic red sandstone. In isolated basins of limestone (II.), in Strasburg, Martick, and Conestoga townships, a good deal of brown hematite was mined, particularly at Safe Harbor. In the great limestone belt a great deal of surface ore has been mined near Christiana and other points; but the principal locality is in Hempfield township, where, over the primal standstone of Chiques ridge, the great Chestnut Hill and other banks have supplied a number of furnaces. The ore lies in, and in most of the banks takes the place of, the upper primal slates at their junction with the limestone. In the south-eastern corner, in the serpentine rocks, some veins of titaniferous magnetic iron-ore have been worked.

Lancaster was one of the first counties to make iron, and contained one of the furnaces in blast in 1728, viz., Kurtz's furnace, built in 1726. The Cornwall furnace, built in 1742 by Peter Grubb. It was blown by a bellows 20 feet 7 inches long, 5 feet 10 inches wide at the breech, and 1 foot 2 inches at the nozzle. Mr. Grubb himself ran it for 3 years, and then leased it on the 11th of June, 1745, with 650 acres of land and the Hopewell forge and 218 acres to *12 persons* for 20 years at a yearly rent of £150 ($633.13). They operated for a *few years only* as the Cornwall Company, and assigned the lease to Jacob Giles, a Quaker of Baltimore, who ran the works actively till the lease expired. Acrelius, 1759, described the mine as "rich and abundant, 40 feet deep, commencing 2 feet under the surface; the ore somewhat mixed with sulphur and copper. Peter Grubb was its discoverer. Here there is a furnace which makes 24 tons a week, and keeps 6 forges regularly at work—2 of his own, 2 belong to Germans in the neighborhood, and 2 in Maryland. The pig iron is carried to the Susquehanna river, thence to Maryland, and finally to England. It belonged to the heirs of the Grubb estate, and is now rented to Gurrit & Co."

In 1765 Peter Grubb resumed the management, residing at Hopewell forge, then thought the most productive property. The whole property remained in the Grubb family till 1798, when Robert Coleman became possessed of over five-sixths of the estate, the rest still belonging to the Grubb family.

At Cornwall the price of pig iron was :—

	£	s.	
In 1780, in Continental money,	300	0	per ton.
In 1789, Pennsylvania currency ($17.30),	6	10	"
In 1796, " " ($28),	10	10	"
In 1800, " " ($26.66),	10	0	"

Robert Coleman was a most successful iron-master, and to him Lancaster county is most indebted for the number and magnitude of its iron-works. The Grubb family began business in 1728, and were distinguished for industry and enterprise. Mount Hope furnace was built in 1786 by Peter Grubb, Jr.; the family still hold it and use Cornwall ore. It was at first 9 feet across the boshes, but like the Warwick furnace has been reduced to 7, and is 27 feet high. It made 800 to 1000 tons a year with cold blast, and is now being altered by A. Bates Grubb, its owner, for hot blast. In 1800 Henry B. Grubb built the Mount Vernon furnace on Conewago creek; it was abandoned in 1852. It produced from the start 50 to 52 tons a week of good forge pig iron, and made a *continuous blast* of 2800 tons. The rate of wages averaged £5 ($13.30) per month, including board.

The old Elizabeth furnace (1796), after Steigel's failure, ran under Robert Coleman and his heirs till 1856, when it was abandoned by G. Dawson Coleman for want of wood.

In 1795, according to Scott's Gazetteer, there were in the county "2 furnaces and 8 forges; the furnaces producing yearly 1200 tons of pig and the forges about so much bar." (Probably means 800 tons bar.)

In 1797 Ebeling enumerates, as existing about 1790, "Coleman's furnace, whose mines lie in the Conewago or Furnace Hills, along with those of Grubb and Speadwell;" 5 forges, Poole (1760), old, (Old's) Martic (1755), Windsor (1745), and Elizabeth (1756). The Speadwell forge was built in 1750, and must be added to the above, making 6 forges in all. The Coleman woodlands "were then 6 to 8 English miles in circumference." Samuel Potts, in his list of 1793, gives 6 forges as the number then in operation.

In 1834 the Conestoga navigation was opened from Lancaster to Safe Harbor, and afforded an easy route to Baltimore, and also the transportation required by the iron-works. In 1833 the county contained, according to A. M. Prevost, 5 charcoal-furnaces, with a product of 5000 tons of pig; 2 rolling-mills, Laurel, Chester Co., and Martic (a forge?), each making 500 tons of bar iron, and 11 forges which produced 2350 tons of bar iron.

In 1840 there were 11 charcoal-furnaces, which made

6912 tons of pig iron; 3 forges and 1 rolling-mill (Cole-mansville, 1828), which made 2090 tons of bar iron, &c.

From Columbia to Chickiswalungo creek, along the bank of the Susquehanna, there lies a group of anthra-cite furnaces, the oldest of them (Shawnee, now Chestnut Hill) built 1844. In 1849 there were 8, the smallest, Shawnee, 8 feet and 28; the largest, Marietta (Mussel-man & Schoenberger) 10 feet and 33. In 1875 the group contained 11 furnaces, the smallest 11 feet bosh (Henry Clay, now St. Charles) and 39½ feet high; the largest 16 feet bosh and 46 feet. They use ores from Lancaster and York counties and from Cornwall. One of them, the Chickies furnace, was described in 1848 by S. S. Haldeman, then senior proprietor, and it illustrates so well the course of improvement that we subjoin the old drawings with one showing the furnace as it now stands.

Furnace No. 1 of the Chickies Iron Company was built in 1846, 32 feet high and 10 feet across the boshes, as illustrated in figures 1 to 3 and by the *old description of the reference letters*. Fig. 1 is a horizontal section through hearth; fig. 2 a vertical section; fig. 3 an ele-vation partly broken to show boiler details, and fig. 4 is a vertical section of the same furnace as it now exists. The main structure is a quadrangular truncated pyramid of masonry, the lower portion of which has an arched passage through the centre of each side, leaving four heavy piers at the corners.

The hearth was built of sandstone (conglomerate) and braced by the narrow inner ends of the piers. Above the hearth eight "sows or iron beams" (*s*, fig. 2) formed the foundation of the in-wall and upper part of the furnace. The hearth was square, 2 feet wide, and 5½ feet long, including the fore-hearth, and flared

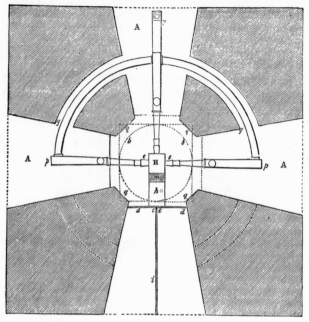

CHICKIES FURNACE.—FIG. I.

A, twier arches.	Hh, hearth.	p, blast-pipe.
B, bosh.	i, dust-plate.	q, square of the hearth.
b, greatest diameter.	k, twier key.	r, space for loam.
c, cinder run.	l, lining.	s, sows.
d, damstone and plate.	m, temp.	t, twiers.
e, tapping-place.	n, sconsh'n.	v, valve in blast-pipe.
f, flues for boilers.	o, hot-blast oven.	w, boilers.
g, passage.		

slightly out upward. At the lower right-hand corner of the hearth, in fig. 2, the old draughtsman has shown the tapping-hole out of its place in the damstone, merely to show its position in the angle of the damstone, hearth, and bottom.

The breast (m, fig. 2) was formed by a large stone called the "sconsh'n." The bosh, shaded vertically, was built of fire-brick, "at a much higher angle than

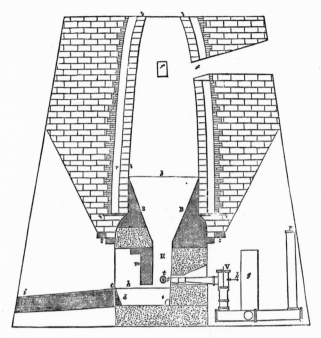

CHICKIES FURNACE.—FIG. 2.

when charcoal is used." "Toward the head of the furnace there are three equi-distant apertures (*f*, fig. 2) *to admit the waste flame*, first under the boilers, then through a return flue in them into a hot oven, which is placed in part upon the top of the stack, posteriorly and laterally. When a separate engine is employed the oven is placed upon the front side of the top, and the flame passes into it by a single aperture." The tunnel-head was closed by a brick chimney (*z*, fig. 3) to protect the men from the heat, and having two large openings for filling.

"The boilers (*ww*, fig. 3) are, in this case, three in number, 26 feet long, 45 inches in diameter, with a

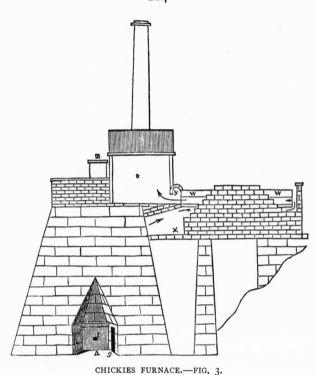

CHICKIES FURNACE.—FIG. 3.

return flue 18 inches in diameter;" and the course of the flame is indicated by the arrows. The boilers are supported on large iron beams, crosswise between which arches are turned. At x, there were cleaning-doors opening downward, and there were other doors along the sides. "The boilers are usually placed in contact with the oven; but the passage y (which extends to the chimneys) is proposed to be left to turn more or less of the flame into the chimneys, which will place the relative distribution of the heat to the oven and boilers under control, a point which seems not to have been hitherto attained. This might also be

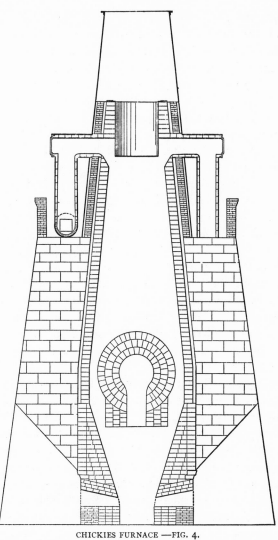

CHICKIES FURNACE — FIG. 4.

accomplished by separate chimneys to the oven and boilers. In either case the chimneys must be supplied with a damper, which is best placed upon the top. When the convenience of a bank cannot be had, it is evident that both boilers and oven might be placed on the ground if the chimney was sufficiently high (not less than 70 feet) and the walls built so as to be free from crevices." (*Am. Jour. of Science and Art, 1848.*)

The hot-oven was built and arched over with brick. It contained 45 U pipes, arranged in three longitudinal rows, on four horizontal circular bed-pipes, a foot in diameter and "12 to 15 feet long," two having one set of openings, the others two sets. The outside U pipes rested on two bed-pipes, and all were connected by cemented sleeve-joints. The pipes were of a flattened, elliptical shape, an inch thick and "4 inches long by 7 or 8 inches wide and about 10 feet high." The bed-pipes had cross-partitions near the centre and the blast was taken from the cold side across at one end through 7 lines of pipes and back at the other end through 8 lines to the same bed-pipe it first left (the partition near the centre separated the cold air from the hot), the eighth line being added to compensate for the expansion of the heated air.

Fig. 4 shows the furnace as it now stands, with 11-foot bosh and a height of 45 feet. The hearth is 4 feet in diameter, the tuyeres 2 feet above the bottom. It is 16 feet to the top of the boshes, and the sheet-iron cylinder in the mouth is 5½ feet deep. All the boilers and ovens are on the ground, the gas being taken, as shown, from both sides of the stack. The gas-flues take only pure, unburnt gas—*no waste flame;* whether that term originated in the Detmold lawsuit or not, the fact that the gas is unburnt is patent to all.

The furnace is now only 20 per cent. larger across the boshes than in the first lining, and is built in the same stack; but a vast improvement has been made since 1846. The gas is fully burned (Detmold, Faber du Faur) under boilers and in stoves, the blast more intense and hotter, and the ores are prepared in ore-washers, unknown in 1846, and less iron wasted in the slag. The coal first used was brought from Wilkes-barre, from the Baltimore vein, by canal to the furnace, which has also used always substantially the same ores (Chestnut Hill and Cornwall) and flux.

BLAST NO. 1, terminated April, 1846.

$2\frac{26}{100}$ tons coal to 1 ton pig iron made.

$2\frac{47}{100}$ tons ore to 1 ton pig iron made.

Capacity of furnace, 30 tons per week.

BLAST NO. 20, terminated October, 1873.

$1\frac{67}{100}$ tons coal to 1 ton pig iron made.

$2\frac{19}{100}$ tons ore to 1 ton pig iron made.

The duration of blasts has steadily increased since anthracite and coke were used, but short blasts, like those of the old charcoal-furnaces, were the rule till about 1860. Before that few furnaces had made a two-years blast, and at Chickies, while 17 blasts were made in 15 years between January 15th, 1846, and June 3d, 1860, only 4, including the present one, have been made in nearly 15 years, from October 16th, 1861, and the present one, beginning December 14th, 1873, is likely to last about two years longer.

In 1856 there were 2 charcoal-furnaces, making 1800 tons of pig iron; 12 anthracite-furnaces, which produced 33,527 tons of pig iron; 11 forges, making, say 2444 tons of blooms; 4 rolling-mills, making 3061 tons of bar iron, &c.; and 1 rail-mill (Safe Harbor, 1848), which made 10,653 tons of rails in 1855 (which were sold prin-cipally to the Pennsylvania Railroad), and has been idle since 1861. The early rails made at these works were very good, some of them have remained over 20 years in the track. A steel-works at Martic made yearly 400 tons of blister and shear steel. In 1873 there were 14 anthracite-furnaces, with a product of 63,498 tons of pig iron; 1 charcoal-furnace (not in blast); 4 rolling-mills, which made 16,869 tons of bar iron, &c.; 2 rail-mills (Columbia and idle Safe Harbor), with a product of 7500 tons; and 2 forges, which made 800 tons of blooms.

LAWRENCE COUNTY, formed in 1850 of parts of Beaver and Mercer. Its geology will be found under those counties. The county depends principally on Lake Superior mines for its ore.

In 1856 there were 2 raw-coal furnaces (Orizaba, 1853; Willieroy, 1854); one of them made 3600 tons, the other being idle. There were also 2 rolling-mills, with a product of say 10,000 tons. One of them, the Cosalo mill, made in 1853 4000 tons of the Winslow split rails, used so largely by the New York Central in its early days. There was also 1 steel-works (Sharon Rolling-mill), with 4 converting-ovens, 20 melting-holes, and a train of rolls, which began in 1855 to make iron direct from the ore by G. Hand Smith's direct process.

In 1873 there were in the county 5 coke-furnaces and 3 raw-coal furnaces, which made 58,745 tons of pig iron; 2 charcoal-furnaces, with a product of 1500 tons; and 3 rolling-mills, which made 14,260 tons.

LEBANON COUNTY, formed in 1813 of parts of Dauphin and Lancaster. It has the same measures as Dauphin county, with practically the same succession and development. It includes part of the lower tongue of the Southern coal basin between the Third and Fourth mountains. The coal, however, cannot be used in blast-furnaces.

The earlier history of its iron-making will be found under Lancaster county. Soon after its separation the Union Canal Company was organized, and the canal was completed in 1827 to Pine Grove, whence a railroad four miles long brought it into connection with the coal-mines of the Dauphin and Pottsville basins. The coal-mines and iron-works were thus supplied with a double outlet, both to the Susquehanna and to the Schuylkill rivers.

The principal production has, however, always centred about the Cornwall mines. This body of ore, though not as rich as some other noted deposits, yet will probably average fifty per cent. of iron, is more easily mined than most others, and is one of the largest in the world. There are three hills of the ore just at the outcrop of the new red measures, above the older limestones, on the south side of the Lebanon (Great or Kittatinny) valley, near Lebanon. The "big" or eastern hill is 312 feet high, the middle and western 98 and 78 feet high, respectively. The extreme thickness is over 500 feet of ore, and it is estimated that 64,000,000 tons of ore are "in sight." It is wrought as an open quarry, principally on the Big and Middle hills, by a series of Y's, which carry the ore-cars around the hill. The ore is worked at various levels, is loosened by powder and thrown into the cars, the tracks being moved as the breast recedes. It is capable of being mined on any scale, 120,000 tons a year having been dug in 1858; 200,000 are now regularly mined, the production being limited to that quantity.

The ore is magnetic, and lies in a single body contained in one large basin of trap. The ore has been very much altered both in the vicinity of the trap and by the atmosphere. It contains a great deal of sulphur, the most weathered ore containing from one-half to one per cent., the ordinary from two to five per cent. It also contains copper oxide and carbonate in considerable quantities, but is very free from phosphorus, of which it contains a mere trace. It had, therefore, for a long time the distinct office of neutralizing the cold-short ores by which it is surrounded, especially before the cost of transportation from New Jersey became moderate, and the corporation (a "tenancy in common" of the Coleman and Grubb families) limited its sale. Now the red-short Morris county magnetic ores have taken its place in the Lebanon and Susquehanna valleys, and the Cornwall owners smelt their own ore, 16 furnaces being worked in connection with this single deposit, though not all of them in its immediate vicinity. With proper treatment to remove copper (and sulphur) it would be a valuable ore for Bessemer steel purposes; the higher grades (I. and II.) of the irons made from it are now largely used for steel; but the lower grades (some II. and III.) contain rather too much sulphur taken in connection with the amount of copper present, often 1.25 per cent. in the pig.

In 1856 the county contained 1 charcoal-furnace (old Cornwall), with a product of 2056 tons; 5 anthracite-furnaces in operation, making 21,628 tons; and 3 forges, which made 808 tons of blooms. The North Lebanon furnaces were built 1848–49 (and a new one building in 1857), and the Cornwall in 1850 and 1855.

In 1873 there were in the county 11 anthracite-furnaces, with a product of 35,308 tons; 1 charcoal-furnace, which made 1189 tons; 2 rolling-mills, with a product of 2900 tons; and 3 forges, which produced 2095 tons of blooms.

LEHIGH COUNTY, formed in 1812 of part of Northampton. The formations include the primary strata
of the South mountain in the south-eastern part of the
county. The primal sandstone has here a very slight
development, the ridges being mainly gneiss, with
several long narrow limestone (II.) basins, the largest
of which is that through which flows the Saucon
creek. The Lower Silurian limestone belt traverses
the county between Millerstown and a short distance
beyond Fogelsville at one side and the South mountain
ridge and Ballietsville on the other. North of the limestone the Hudson river slates extend to the Kittatinny
mountain. The county abounds in productive mines
of brown hematite ore in the limestone belts. The
ore occurs at the junction of the South mountain with
the limestone (Emaus, &c.), and at the contact of the
latter with the slates (Ballietsville and Fogelsville), and
on the limestone in thick deposits, principally worked
on a line from north of Allentown to Fogelsville, and
so on west through the "East Penn" valley. Magnetic ore occurs in the gneiss, but has been little mined,
owing to the irregularity of the veins.

The first furnace in the county was the Hampton
charcoal-furnace, built in 1809 at the head of the north
branch of Perkiomen creek; this furnace long worked
alone.

The discovery of the use of anthracite gave the
county a cheap fuel, and its own ores sufficed for the
earlier work; but the proximity of the great deposits of
rich ore in New Jersey at the *debouchure* of the Lehigh
valley secured a plentiful supply of ore for a great and
rapid development of manufacture. The Crane Iron
Company were the first to build furnaces, the first
one built in 1840 being of large size and constructed

expressly to smelt iron with anthracite by means of hot blast. This company added furnace after furnace in 1842, 1846, two in 1850, and in 1867. The Allentown Company began in 1846, and now has 5 stacks; the Lehigh Valley Iron Company in 1853, now has 3 stacks, and the Thomas Iron Company, beginning in 1855, now has 6 stacks. These four companies control 20 stacks, the smaller of which is 11 feet in diameter at the boshes and 45 feet high, and the largest 20 feet by 60 feet high.

In 1856 there were in the county 1 charcoal-furnace, making 550 tons; 12 anthracite-furnaces, which made 65,855 tons; and 1 rolling-mill, with a product of 200 tons yearly.

In 1873 there were 27 anthracite-furnaces, producing 216,092 tons of pig iron; 1 charcoal-furnace; 3 rolling-mills, with a product of 23,203 tons; and 1 rail-mill (Allentown), which made 20,865 tons of rails.

The history of the use of anthracite coal in smelting iron properly belongs here. Very early attempts to use anthracite were made by stockholders (Josiah White and Erskine Hazard) of the Lehigh Coal and Navigation Company, at Mauch Chunk, in 1820, in a furnace built for the purpose, but the efforts were wholly unsuccessful. These gentlemen, at that time the principal managers of the navigation company, had previously, in 1813, been manufacturers of wire at the Falls of Schuylkill, above Philadelphia, using Richmond, Va., coal. They were always anxious to use anthracite, both to obtain cheaper iron and a market for coal. Cold blast can, however, be used successfully with anthracite, for somewhat long periods at least, with no worse result than decreasing the product of the furnace. Nicolas Hunter, of Moselem, Berks county, made for some time a cold-blast anthracite car-wheel iron in the furnace in which he ordinarily used hot blast, changing from one to the other, according to the demand. In ordinary manufacture, however, it is true that the use of hot blast alone made it possible to use anthracite coal economically.

On December 19th, 1833, Dr. Frederick W. Geisenheimer, of New York, received a patent for smelting anthracite with hot blast under such pressure as the density of anthracite made requisite. Neilson's patent for hot blast in general was taken out in 1828. Geisenheimer claimed the use of anthracite in deoxidating iron-ore and in carbonizing the iron when reduced, and adding carbon to bar iron to make steel; smelting the deoxidized ore with anthracite; refining by use of anthracite; smelting raw ores with anthracite; the use of heated air applied "in connection with the principle discovered by me," in the necessary quantity and density. Iron was smelted with anthracite in Wales, at the Yniscedevin works, by Mr. George Crane, who took out a patent in America, November 29th, 1838, and is understood to have bought Geisenheimer's patent. Mr. Crane began on the 5th of February, 1837, and the first account of his operations reached this country in the report of the September (1837) meeting of the British Association.

In the fall and winter of 1837 Messrs. Baughman, Giteau & High fitted up the unsuccessful experimental furnace at Mauch Chunk to work with hot blast. Their first trial succeeded surprisingly, and they built a new small furnace near the weigh-lock at Mauch Chunk, which is the one referred to in the tables below.

In 1836 Mr. Solomon W. Roberts went to Cardiff, Wales, as inspector of rails ordered by the Philadelphia and Reading and other railroads, visited Mr. Crane's works in May, 1837, promptly notified his uncle, Josiah White, of the entirely successful use of anthracite, and returned in November to Philadelphia, bringing the details of Crane's plans and specimens illustrative of the process. Mr. Roberts declined to take up the manufacture, and recommended that one of Crane's associates should be employed. In accordance with this advice, Erskine Hazard, of the Lehigh Coal and Navigation Company, went to Wales, in November, 1838. " He ordered such machinery as was necessary to be made for the company,—under the direction of George Crane, the inventor,—and engaged Mr. David Thomas, who was familiar with the process, to take charge of the erection of the works and the manufacture of the iron." (*Richardson, Memoir Josiah White.*)

Mr. Thomas arrived in June, 1839, the (Lehigh) Crane Company was formed, and on July 9th began at Cata-sauqua the erection of the furnace referred to in the tables below, which made its first iron on July 4th, 1840; the furnace (11 feet by 45 feet) is still in use. Mr. Thomas was entirely successful from the start and his plans were extensively copied. Mr. Thomas founded the Thomas Iron Works in 1855, and is justly honored for his eminent services in making the manufacture of anthracite iron a commercial success.

The Pioneer furnace of Pottsville built in 1838 by William Lyman, Burd Patterson, and others, made in 1839 iron with anthracite. Previous to this time Messrs. Burd Patterson, Nicholas Biddle, and others *had offered $5000 to the first person who could keep an anthracite-furnace iu blast three months.* Mr. Lyman succeeded and won the prize in the winter of 1839. Mr. Thomas was present when it was blown in, and it was under the charge of Mr. B. Perry, who afterwards blew in the Roaring Creek and the Columbia furnaces.

Thomas Chambers stated (1846) that Mr. Lyman made no use of Mr. Crane's experience, and yet his success was complete and perfect in his prize-blast of ninety days' (December, 1839) continuance at Pottsville. The feat was almost incredible in an inferior furnace, with a weak blast. Subsequently the furnace did badly, as it was supplied " with ores of almost every variety, mixed or used separately without proper discrimination," sometimes it was alleged the supply of ore becoming totally exhausted. Experiments with a view of using blast heated by being *blown through a fire in a close furnace*, thus sending in the products of combustion, were total failures; the cinder became black, the hearth was cut out, and the furnace was blown out. A semi-circular tube apparatus (Calder oven) was then put in with success. The average run was stated to have been as follows :—

Coal, . 1000 lbs. ⎫ *Charge*—and from 18 to 20
Ore, . 1750 lbs. ⎬ charges per 24 hours, yielding
Limestone, 800 lbs. ⎭ 34 tons of iron per week.

Niles' Register, December 14th, 1839, quotes the *Pottsville Journal* as announcing the shipment from that place of the first load of anthracite iron—54 tons 10 cwt. from Lyons (*sic*.) anthracite-iron furnace.

On January 18th, 1840, Mr. Lyman gave a dinner at Pottsville, to celebrate the successful completion of the prize blast,—an event characterized by Thomas Biddle as our second Declaration of Independence. Nicholas Biddle, in a happy speech, compared the effect of hot-blast on the ores and coal which would not yield their treasure to a cold blast to that of the sun on the traveler, who only wrapped himself the closer against the cold wind, but could not resist the sunshine. He showed how the iron trade of Eastern Pennsylvania was then embarrassed by the scarcity and high price of charcoal and the cost of difficult transportation from the interior. Hence the country had to pay Europeans for its iron, and in two years, 1836–37, had imported upward of $24,000,000 worth of iron and steel; while in the very farthest depths of the mines they had visited that morning the coal was hauled over English rails. Pennsylvania had taken, in seven years, 80,000 tons of iron, excluding hardware and cutlery, but including 49,000 tons of rails, worth $3,500,000. Our mechanics, said Mr. Biddle, though they receive higher pay, do more work than foreigners. Why then should we not, with all our resources, turn our ores into money at the furnace and the mill, now we have found out the way, and pay our debts, as England does, with coal and iron! He proposed, "Old Pennsylvania: Her sons, like her soil, a rough outside, but solid stuff within; plenty of coal to warm her friends; plenty of iron to cool her enemies." Mr. Lyman afterwards toasted Burd Patterson, "the gentleman who originally projected the anthracite experiment of Pottsville, and the firm friend of every enterprise which can advance the interests of Pennsylvania."

The subjoined table contains the most interesting facts contained in Professor Johnson's table of the pioneer anthracite-furnaces. It will be noted that the furnaces all have *square hearths*. Alexander notes the use of a circular hearth at Merthyr Tydfil, Wales, in 1840, as an unusual thing. It may be added, too, that the Shamokin furnace used the old machinery of the abandoned coke-furnace at Farrandsville.

No. of Furnace	Name and Situation of Furnace	Proprietor	Occupant	When built	Date of commencing blast with anthracite.	Dimensions of stack in feet.			Pig Iron produced per week. Tons.	Temperature of blast, Fahrenheit.	No. of tuyeres.	Pressure, pounds per square inch.	Nature of Ores used.	
						Height.	Diam. of boshes.	Square of the New Hearth					Locality and character.	Yield per cent.
1	Mauch Chunk	Baughman, Guiteau & Co.	Owners...	1838	Aug. 27, 1838.	21½	5½	1 5-12	8	450	2	2	Hematite, } N. J........ Magnetic, }	40 to 70
2	Pottsville........	Marshall, Kellogg & Co..	Owners...	1838	July 10, 1839,	35	8¾	3½	28	600	3	1½	Carbonate and hema- } tite... .... }	25 to 50
3	Roaring Creek..	Burd Patterson & Co......	Dr. Steinberger...	1838-9	May 18, 1840,	30	8½		40	650	3	2½	Fossiliferous peroxide, } of Bloomsburg....... }	50 to 64
4	Phenixville..	Messrs. Reeves............	Owners...	1837	June 17, 1840,	33	8	3×6½	28	700	3	1½	Hydrated peroxide......	38 to 50
5	Danville... ..	Biddle, Chambers & Co...	Owners...	1838-9	April, 1840,	30	7½		35	600	2	2¾	Calcareous peroxide, of } Danville .... }	45 to 60
6	Crane Iron } Works, near } Allentown.. }	Crane Iron Company.....	Owners...	1839-40	July 4, 1840,	40	12	3½	50	600	3	2½	Hydrated peroxide, } near the works...... }	40 to 55
7	Columbia, at } Danville... }	George Patterson........	J. P. & J. Groves.	1839	July 2, 1840,	33	8½	3½	31½	612	3	3	Calcareous fossiliferous } peroxide .... }	45 to 60
8	Montour, at } Danville. No. }	Biddle, Chambers & Co...	Owners...	1840	July 11, 1841,	32	12	4	70	612	3	4	Fossil, calcareous, and } silicious peroxide.... }	33 to 60
9	Montour, at } Danville. No. } 2........ }	Biddle, Chambers & Co...	Owners...	1840	August, 1841,	32	12	4			3		Fossil, calcareous, and } silicious peroxide.... }	33 to 60
10	Shamokin........	Shamokin Iron Company..	Owners...	1840		42½	12	4			3		Carbonate and Dan- } ville fossiliferous.... }	33 to 60
11 } 12 } 13 } 14 }	Stanhope, N. J..	Stanhope Iron Company..	Owners...	1840-41	April 5, } 1841, }	30	10	3½	56	600	3	3	Magnetic, of Irondale...	50 to 70

The work of the 8 furnaces detailed is represented by
1 ton of iron to 2.24 tons ore, 1.57 tons coal, and 0.95
ton limestone. In addition, the Danville and Columbia
used 4 and 3½ cwt. of coal to raise steam, and the
Roaring Creek, Danville, Crane, Columbia, Montour,
and Stanhope furnaces used 0.23 ton coal for heating
blast for 1 ton of iron, hence the total coal used averaged only 1.8 tons per ton of iron. The coal charges
varied from 336 lbs. (Crane, No. 1) to 1050 lbs.
(Montour.)

I am enabled, by the courtesy of Mr. Joshua Hunt, to
quote the details of the first two blasts of the Crane No.
1, the draft of which has unfortunately been lost. The
blast was stopped in 26¾ weeks by a destructive flood,
which broke the dam, and covered the water-wheel used
with mud. The amount of iron was 1087 tons 15 cwt.
1 qr. 13 lbs., or 41¼ tons per week; coal, 2.04 (*including
0.54 tons for hot blast*); ore, 2.33; limestone, 1.20 tons per
ton of iron. In the second blast of 63⅝ weeks the coal
for hot blast amounted to 15 cwt. per ton of iron, and
the average was: coal, 2.16; ore, 1.84, and limestone,
0.77 tons per ton of iron, of which in all 3316.58 tons,
or 52.05 tons per week, were made. In this last blast
the coal charge was 392 pounds, and with this same
charge No. 2 furnace made on its first blast, beginning
November 12th, 1842, during 71¼ weeks, an average of
76.34 tons of iron a week, with 1.91 tons of coal per ton,
out of 47.8 per cent. ores. Compare with this the last
work of No. 6 furnace, the product of which—1604.5
tons in 5 consecutive weeks, and 353 tons in 1 week (over
nine-tenths of all being No. 1 *x* grade)—is thought the
largest yet made in an anthracite-furnace. Dimensions
are 60 feet high, *with open top*, 18 feet bosh, 6 tuyeres
4 inches diameter, and blast at a pressure of 8 pounds.

In 6 months, ending June 30th, 1876, the product was :—

IRON MADE.			AVERAGES.
No. 1 *x* foundry, .	6,761	tons.	1.52 tons coal per ton iron.
No. 2 *x* foundry, .	713.50	"	2.19 tons ore per ton iron.
No. 2 gray forge, .	74	"	1.45 tons limestone per ton iron.
No. 3 mottled, .	78.50	"	293.34 tons iron per week.
Total, . .	7,627	tons.	

By act approved May 25th, 1839, Henry High, J. Baughman, Julius Guiteau, F. C. Lowthrop, and Ed. L. Taylor were incorporated into a stock company, under the title of the " Anthracite Iron Company," with a capital of $500,000, which perished in the financial crisis of 1842.

The following letter explains the manner in which Baughman, Guiteau & Co. conducted their experiments :—

"BEAVER MEADOW, November 9th, 1840.

"SIR :—Agreeably to a request of Colonel Henry High, of Reading, I send you a hastily-written statement of the experiments made by Baughman, Giteau & Co., in the smelting of iron-ore with anthracite coal as a fuel.

"During the fall and winter of the year 1837, Messrs. Joseph Baughman, Julius Guiteau, and Henry High, of Reading, made their first experiment in smelting iron-ore with anthracite coal, in an old furnace at Mauch Chunk, temporarily fitted up for the purpose. They used about 80 per cent. of anthracite, and the result was such as to surprise those who witnessed it (for it was considered as an impossibility even by iron-masters), and to encourage the persons engaged in it to go on. In order, therefore, to test the matter more thoroughly, they built a furnace on a small scale, near the Mauch Chunk Weigh-Lock, which was completed during the month of July, 1838.

"DIMENSIONS.—Stack, 21 ½ feet high, 22 feet square at the base.

" Boshes, 5 ½ feet across.

" Hearth, 14 by 16 inches in the square and 4 feet 9 inches from the dam-stone to the back.

" Blowing apparatus consisted of 2 cylinders, each 6 feet diameter ; a receiver, same diameter and about 2 ½ feet deep; stroke 11 inches; each piston making from 12 to 15 strokes per minute.

" An overshot water-wheel, diameter 14 feet, length of bucket 3 ½ feet, number of buckets 36, revolutions per minute from 12 to 15.

" The blast was applied August 27th, and the furnace kept in blast until September 10th, when they were obliged to stop in consequence of the apparatus for heating the blast proving to be too temporary. Several tons of iron were produced of Nos. 2 and 3 quality. I do not recollect the proportion of anthracite used. Temperature of blast did not exceed 200 degrees Fahrenheit.

" A new and good apparatus for heating the blast was next procured (it was at this time I became a partner in the firm of Baughman, Guiteau & Co.), consisting of 200 feet in length of cast-iron pipes 1 ½ inches thick ; it was placed in a brick chamber at the tunnel-head, and heated by a flame issuing thence.

" The blast was again applied about the last of November, 1838, and the furnace worked remarkably well for 5 weeks, exclusively with anthracite coal. We were obliged, however, for want of ore, to blow out on the 12th of January, 1839. During this experiment our doors were open to the public, and we were watched very closely, both day and night, for men could hardly believe what they saw with their own eyes, so incredulous was the public in regard to the matter at that time.

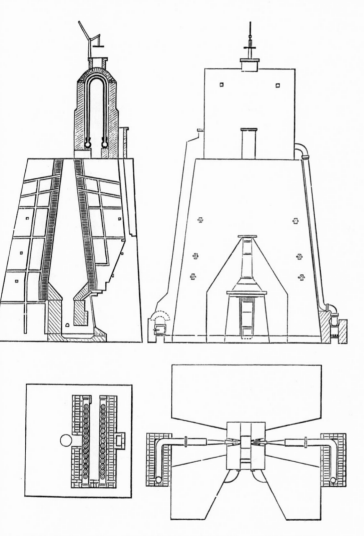

FIRST FURNACE USING ANTHRACITE SUCCESSFULLY.   MAUCH CHUNK.

Some iron-masters expressed themselves astonished that a furnace *could work* while using unburnt, unwashed, frozen ore, such as was put into our furnace.

"The amount of iron produced was about 1½ tons per day, when working best, of Nos. 1, 2, and 3 quality. The temperature of the blast was about 400 degrees Fahrenheit.

"The following season we enlarged the hearth to 19 by 21 inches and 5 feet 3 inches from the dam-stone to the back of hearth; and on July 26th the furnace was again put in blast, and continued in blast until November 2d, 1839, a few days after the dissolution of our firm, when it was blown out in good order. For about 3 months we used no other fuel than anthracite, and produced about 100 tons of iron, of good Nos. 1, 2, and 3 quality. When working best the furnace produced about 2 tons per day. Temperature of the blast was from 400 to 600 degrees Fahrenheit. The following ores were used by us, viz.:—'Pipe ore,' from Miller's mine, a few miles from Allentown; 'brown hematite,' commonly called *top mine* or surface ore; 'rock ore,' from Dickerson's mine, in New Jersey; and 'Williams township ore,' in Northampton county. The last-mentioned ore produced a very strong iron and most beautiful cinder.

"The above experiments were prosecuted under the most discouraging circumstances, and, if we gain anything by it, it can only be the credit of acting the part of pioneers in a praiseworthy undertaking.

"Most respectfully, sir,
"Your obedient servant,
"F. C. LOWTHROP.
"Professor WALTER R. JOHNSON,
"*Philadelphia.*"

The illustration is copied from a tracing of the original drawing left unchanged except as to the bricks, which could not be shown on this small scale. The horizontal and vertical sections do not agree as to the dam. The hearth bottom was purposely hollowed out.

The foregoing pages describe the first production of anthracite pig, but it seems certain that so long before any of these experiments as 1828 *wrought iron had been made with anthracite direct from the ore.* This was done "at his works in New Jersey" by B. B. Howell, who in 1831 was secretary of the Iron Trade Committee, and wrote the report submitted to the convention of Friends of Domestic Industry, in New York. The furnace was a "high bloomery" or veritable German "Wolfofen," but with a forehearth like a blast-furnace and the novel arrangement of 2 sets of tuyeres, one of which was to reduce the ore to a carburetted metal to be refined by the lower set; the forehearth being used like a forge, and the burden in the upper or furnace part held up with bars while the loup was withdrawn. (*Frank. Inst. Jour.*, N. S., vol. 3, page 138.) Mr. Howell succeeded in converting ore perfectly into malleable iron with anthracite exclusively, and made bar iron as good as that of the neighboring forges and turned it into nails without even letting it cool. Dr. Thomas P. Jones, the editor of the *Institute Journal*, vouches for these facts, and stated he had nails and a piece of bar made from the first bloom produced. Hence, in one way, Mr. Howell anticipated everyone in the use of anthracite, and even Geisenheimer's claims seem to relate to this method as improved by the use of hot blast.

LUZERNE COUNTY, formed in 1786 of part of Northumberland. The measures of the county are the anthracite coal measures and the rocks immediately underlying them. There is very little iron-ore in the county. The carbonate ores of the Umbral red shales (XI.) were opened on the lands of the Lackawanna Iron and Coal Company, at Kingston Gap, &c., but very little indeed is now mined, and New Jersey and New York magnetites are mainly used. It is a singular thing that there are not now any, and never have been but 3 furnaces in the anthracite regions using local ore (carbonate) with the coal. The Shamokin, and the Schuylkill Valley furnaces ran, for a short while only, on local ores, and the Pioneer furnace hardly attempted their use. The carbonate ore or black bands are almost absent in the anthracite fields.

In 1797 Ebeling records "2 furnaces working bog ore." These were Alden's (1778), on Nanticoke creek, and 1 on Roaring brook, near Scranton, built by Dr. William Hooke Smith and James Sutton. Both were abandoned in 1828.

Thatcher T. Payne, Esq. owned the Wyoming Mill at Wilkesbarre, built in 1842 for railroad iron; hence this mill shares with Brady's Bend the credit of making the first rails.

In 1856 there were in the county 1 charcoal-furnace, the product of which was 300 tons; 5 anthracite-furnaces, which make 11,500 tons; 1 forge, on Nescopec creek (1824), which made 225 tons of bars and blooms, and 1 rail-mill (Lackawanna Iron and Coal Company), which produced 11,338 tons of rails.

In 1873 there were 5 anthracite-furnaces, making 47,540 tons; 1 rail-mill, with a product of 40,384 tons (including 288 tons of bar iron), and 1 Bessemer steel-works, started October 23d, 1875. It belongs to the type of which the Pennsylvania Steel Company works were the first in the State, followed by the Edgar Thomson, and is of equal capacity. I regret my limits forbid a detailed description. All these belong to the Lackawanna Company. Their rolling-mill was built in 1844, and in 1856 had 47 furnaces and 3 trains of rolls. The first blast-furnace, built 1842, used anthracite, and was abandoned before 1856. The furnaces include one 18 feet bosh by 80 feet high, and one 23 feet bosh by 67 feet high; the older ones being only 48 feet high.

LYCOMING COUNTY, formed in 1796 of part of Northumberland. The measures of this county include outcrops of strata from the Lower Silurian limestones (II.) to the conglomerate floor of the coal measures. The tops of some hills carry small patches of coal, accompanied by fire-clay and iron-ore strata, and a belt of brown silicious iron-ore, in the Devonian (Vergent) shales, has been mined at Larry's Creek, Pine Creek, &c.

The coal basin is about 10 miles long in all on an extension of the second basin from Towanda, principally worked near Ralston and Astonville. The ore is that of the Umbral red shales (XI.). Here, just under the conglomerate, are a 2-foot vein of carbonate ore and a 1-foot and a 2-foot course of ore-ball, the latter coldshort.

Iron-making began in this county before 1840, the Astonville furnace and another on Pine creek having then been in operation. In 1840 there were in the county 4 charcoal-furnaces and 3 forges (Heshbon, 1828, and Hepburn, 1830) and bloomeries.

In 1856 there were 3 charcoal-furnaces, which made 1075 tons; 1 anthracite-furnace, with a product of about 750 tons; 2 forges, that produced 320 tons of bars and blooms, and 2 rolling-mills, which made 700 tons yearly.

In 1857 the Astonville furnace changed from charcoal to anthracite, and the Ralston furnace was built

for anthracite in 1854, but was abandonod after two unsuccessful blasts. Both were built to use Ralston ore
(XI.), but there was no money in it, as it yielded raw
only 25 per cent., though it cost in 1858 only $1.25 per
ton to mine.

In 1873 the 2 rolling-mills alone remained and made
900 tons.

MERCER COUNTY, formed in 1800 of part of Allegheny. The county lies chiefly in the lower strata of
the bituminous coal formation, and coal-measure carbonates occur in many parts in the south of the county.
A line from Kinzua to Sandy Lake in Mercer, and
Youngstown, marks the northern outcrop of the lowest
bituminous coals of the Sixth basin. But below it,
and below (Rogers) or in the conglomerate, the Sharon
group of coal measures comes in with a block-coal seam,
varying from 2 to 5 feet thick. The same coal supports the blast-furnaces of the Mahoning valley, in Ohio.
The coal is a semi-cannel, of slaty structure, quite free
from sulphur, and of such character that it works well
raw in the furnace.

In 1843 there were 2 charcoal-furnaces smelting local
ores (Erie, 1842, (?) Anandale, 1843, abandoned 1849),
and 1 rolling-mill and nail-factory; but the iron industry languished till the completion of the Erie Extension
canal, which developed the coal trade and brought in
other ores. The region now depends almost entirely
on Lake Superior ores.

In 1845 3 raw-coal furnaces were built; in 1846 were
added 4 others; 1 more in 1847, and a ninth in 1848.
They varied from 9 to 11½ feet boshes,—only one, the
Big Bend, having 7½ feet bosh.

It seems clear that in this county, at Clarksville, and
in the Clay furnace (8½ and 37 feet, two 3-inch tuyeres,

abandoned 1860) of Himrod, Vincent & Co., the first iron was made with raw coal. Blown in July, 1845, as a charcoal-furnace, as apparent from its size, it was obliged, after a few months, to use coke made of the block coal, owing to a scarcity of charcoal. The coal could scarcely be expected to coke, and so, owing to a difficulty with his coke-burners, Mr. Himrod *charged coal raw* and made good iron.

But the first furnace *specially built to use raw coal* in the United States was the Mahoning, Lowell, Mahoning county, Ohio, 10 miles west of New Castle. This was built in 1845 by the elder Mr. Crowther for Wilkinson & Co., of Buffalo. The furnace went into blast August 8th, 1846, and has used raw coal ever since. The *Turnbull Democrat*, of Warren, Ohio, on August 15th, 1846, described the blowing in with the conclusion "that to these gentlemen (Wilkinson, Wilkes & Co.) belongs the honor of being the *first persons in the United States* who have succeeded in putting a furnace in blast with *raw bituminous coal.*" Mr. Wilkinson wrote to Prof. J. P. Lesley, in 1858, saying the "raw coal was *first used* at Mahoning furnace in August, 1846, and we used it because its analysis was similar to that of the Splint coal of Scotland." Mr. Wilkinson and his brothers seem to be entitled to the credit, as they built a *large furnace* (12 feet bosh and 45 feet, five 3-inch tuyeres) specially for the purpose, and risked a large amount in the enterprise. This was, too, the *first* furnace in the country which *successfully brought the waste gas down to hot-blast ovens and boilers on the ground*, under the direction of Mr. Crowther. The Ellicotts, at Baltimore, in 1841, and others, had fired boilers on the ground, but their stoves were on top of the furnace. This improvement was a legitimate outgrowth of Faber du Faur's plans. The Mahoning furnace had two gas-pipes, one to the oven and one to the boilers. The hot ovens had four sets of round siphon-pipes, 4 inches in diameter and 10 feet high, in four ranks. Only one ton of coal a week was used in addition to the gas. The boilers were fired with gas introduced *behind* the bridge wall; "two tons of coal a day additional were used to help make steam." The tunnel-head was of course open, so the draft-stacks must have been low, for now, in the same region, with open tops and high draft-stacks, so much gas is got that a good deal goes entirely to waste. The general engineering of the furnace was very good, and its work carefully regulated, for the charges were all measured at the tunnel-head.

In 1856 there were 1 charcoal-furnace, which made no iron, and 4 remained of the 9 raw-coal furnaces, 3 of which made 4464 tons of pig iron. The hard coal-measure ores of Newcastle and other localities proved unprofitable and insufficient, and in 1856 Lake Superior specular ore began to come in. Since that time iron-making has flourished in proportion to the quantity of lake ore introduced.

In 1873 there were in the county 22 raw-coal furnaces, with a product of 96,710 tons of pig iron; 5 rolling-mills, which make 13,943 tons, and 1 rail-mill, which produced 5073 tons of iron rails. In regard to the number and size of its blast-furnaces, Mercer is now the second county in the State, Lehigh being the first. Berks county has, however, as many furnaces (18 anthracite, 5 charcoal), but their capacity is much less.

The whole Shenango valley region, so called, in Lawrence and Mercer counties, contains 32 furnaces, and the contiguous Mahoning valley, in Ohio, contains 22 furnaces, or 40 in all, using raw coal mainly; the

Lehigh valley group contains 50 anthracite-furnaces. The greatest productions were those of 1872—She-nango, 160,188 net tons; Mahoning, 200,785 net tons; and Lehigh, 449,665 net tons; the totals for 1875 being 137,025, 115,993, and 280,360 net tons, respectively.

MIFFLIN COUNTY, formed in 1789 of parts of Cumberland and Northumberland. The surface of the county is greatly broken by the upheavals which formed the Allegheny chain, and includes the Chemung slates with little ore. The Lower Silurian limestone is brought up in the Kischicoquillas valley, between Jack's and Stone mountains, and extending across the county. This valley contains a great deal of brown hematite. The Clinton shales, with their fossil ore, have important outcrops, and the Levant or Medina, with its sandstone ore, as seen but not worked, are exposed in every mountain in the county. The fossil ore is best developed in the middle Juniata valley and in Ferguson's valley, west of Lewistown.

In this county there were, in 1797, 1 furnace and 4 forges. The early works have disappeared without a relic. The Freedom forge was built in 1810, and in 1856 was one of the largest in the State, having 8 fires and five hammers, and making, in 1856, 930 tons of blooms and 380 tons of bars. The Brookland forge was built in 1839. In 1850 there were 5 furnaces and 2 forges, all out of blast except the Freedom forge.

In 1856 the county contained 1 charcoal-furnace (Brookland, 1839), with a product of 520 tons (the Matilda, 1838, stopped 1855); 2 anthracite-furnaces, which made 4400 tons of pig iron; 2 forges, producing 1810 tons of blooms and bars,—one of them making wire billets.

In 1873 there were 3 anthracite-furnaces (the old

Matilda rebuilt, and Glamorgan 2, 1853 and 1872), with a product of 10,024 tons; 1 charcoal-furnace, which made 1841 tons; 1 forge and rolling-mill (Freedom, now Logan), making 1433 tons, and 1 cast-steel works (William Butcher), which made 1519 tons.

The Freedom and Greenwood works have for many years been consolidated, and in 1868 a Bessemer works with 2 five-ton converters, a rail-mill, and the Emma furnace were built mainly to use the company's ore on Stone creek. The Bessemer works did not prove successful because the ores were not sufficiently free from phosphorus, and by the time this had been ascertained the working capital had been absorbed (1871) in bad, unavailable steel. The machinery of the Bessemer works is now at Joliet, Illinois, and the old concern was reorganized, under the title of the Logan Iron and Steel Company. The Freedom Works, originally built to supply railroad material, have thus, at various times, made almost every variety of it, except iron rails and including cold-blast pig for car wheels. The William Butcher Steel-works, which built a tyre-mill and leased part of the Logan machinery, make cast-steel tires and axles. They have 28 4-pot melting-holes and a very fine double-acting hammer with wrought-iron frame.

The Freedom forge has produced some of the very best wrought iron in the country out of cold-blast charcoal metal worked in a "sinking fire" or forge. Mr. William G. Nielson, lately manager of the Logan Company, informed me that their furnaces used, with cold blast, 205 bushels of charcoal per ton of iron. When this metal is refined directly, a forge-fire makes 6 loups or about half a ton per turn, and only runs one turn a day, so that its product is 3 tons a week. White iron is seldom used on account of the inferiority of the product, but hot-blast pig, refined in run-out fires, is now generally used, and on this iron a forge produces 1 ton a day. The hammers are 4-ton cast-iron helve hammers, or wooden helve hammers weighing 1500 pounds. With cold-blast pig the quantity of charcoal used per ton of blooms is 125 bushels.

In 1850 John A. Wright described the iron industry of Mifflin, Huntingdon, and Centre making "Juniata" iron as a very important district. Twelve ranges of mountains furnish vast bodies of woodland unfit for cultivation and the wood made strong charcoal. Huntingdon county supplied Pittsburg, the others depended on the Philadelphia markets. The iron was, and is, equal to the best Swedish or Russian. The stock of these charcoal-furnaces was in preparation 20 months before it was used, the year's stock being worth $25,000 to $35,000. The average number of men employed at a furnace making 1000 tons a year was not less than 70, and of horses 50. The proprietor's store sold goods to the value of about $8000. The furnace cost $20,000, required 7000 acres of woodland counted at $1 per acre, $10,000 was invested in teams and outfit, and $20,000 working capital was needed for the business of one furnace; a total outlay of $57,000.

The average cost of pig iron in the three counties was then $20, exclusive of interest, and it then sold in Philadelphia at $25 per ton—that is, at a loss, for the average freight was $5.25 and expenses $2.25, making $27.50. The competition of anthracite and coke iron had already begun to tell, and unusual quantities of British iron were sold at any price.

In 1831 Hardman Phillips and George Valentine found, in the counties of Centre and Huntingdon, the following consumption of produce per ton of bar iron and castings made:—

20 bushels wheat and rye, average 75 cents,	$15 00
57 pounds pork, average 5 cents,	2 85
43 pounds beef, average 4 cents,	1 72
10 pounds butter, average 12½ cents,	1 25
2 bushels potatoes, average 30 cents,	60
½ ton hay, average $7,	3 50
For every 10 tons bar iron one horse is employed one whole year, worth $100, and one horse dies per annum out of every seven so employed, causing a charge of	1 43
For fruit and vegetables,	1 00
	$27 35

These figures were derived from actual returns, and at that time these counties were the "most extensively engaged in the manufacture of iron in Pennsylvania."

MONTGOMERY COUNTY, formed in 1784 of part of Philadelphia. It lies in the primary gneiss formations to the south and the New Red shales and sandstones to the north, which cover two-thirds of the county. A Lower Silurian limestone basin, stretching from Abingdon across the Schuylkill above and below Conshohocken, furnishes most of the ore mined in the county, and in it brown hematite is dug at many places. Magnetic ore occurs on Perkiomen creek.

In 1797 Ebeling records 4 forges in operation. Valley forge (old at the Revolution); Gulf's, in Lower Merion; 1 in Salford (Green Lane, 1733), and 1 at Pottsgrove (Glasgow, 1750), formerly McCall's. Scull mentions, also, Swift's and Mayberrie's forges.

In 1856 there were in the county 9 anthracite-furnaces, with a product of 24,512 tons of pig iron; 3 forges, which made 780 tons of blooms; and 9 rolling-mills, which produced 8794 tons of bar and boiler-plate yearly.

In 1873 there were 14 anthracite-furnaces, with a product of 103,419 tons of pig iron, and 10 rolling-mills, which made 20,866 tons of boiler-plate and sheet iron.

The iron trade of this county remained weak till the anthracite of the Schuylkill basins was brought down. This was done about 1840, and the Springmill furnace was built in 1844. The Plymouth and William Penn, No. 1, followed in 1845, and the Merion in 1848. These furnaces all worked ores found in the limestone basin of Chester and Montgomery counties, which have proved limited, and much ore is now imported by water from New Jersey and the Hudson river; but the proximity to the markets of Philadelphia has insured the gradual increase of the district.

MONTOUR COUNTY, formed in 1850 of part of Columbia, under which county its geology is described.

The history of the earlier iron-making of the county will be found under Columbia and Lehigh counties.

In 1856 there were 5 anthracite-furnaces in the county, producing 21,850 tons; a sixth, the Franklin, was built in 1840, and has lain idle since 1855. The rolling-mill product of the county was chiefly confined to rails, there being, in 1855, 2 rail-mills, the Rough and Ready, afterward the National, producing 5259 tons, and the Montour Iron-works (now Pennsylvania Iron-works), producing 17,538 tons.

In 1873 the county contained 7 anthracite-furnaces, with a product of 30,692 tons of pig iron, and 2 rail-mills (Danville) on light rails only, and Pennsylvania, with a product of 32,220 tons of iron rails; another rail-mill, the National, lay idle, but has since resumed as the Hancock Company. The Co-operative (1871) ran as a puddle-mill only, till 1874, but now is finished as a rail-mill.

The ores of the county are chiefly fossiliferous, found along Montour's ridge; but their quantity is comparatively limited, and for any very large production the county must depend on other ores. The quantity of soft fossil ore in Montour's ridge is, however, vastly in excess of the estimate of Rogers. He took the workable breast at 30 yards only, but experience at Frankstown and elsewhere has shown not less than 70 to 130 yards of soft ore. Rogers' estimate may therefore be safely trebled, and is also affected by the fact that at Bedford vertical beds of fossil ore have been found, soft and workable to water-level, contrary to Rogers' opinion.

NORTHAMPTON COUNTY, formed in 1752 of part of Bucks county. This county lies in Lower Silurian measures, the gneiss of the South mountain with its isolated limestone basins of the Saucon, Frey's creek, &c., reaches to the Lehigh where the limestone (II.) begins stretching northward to Belvidere and to Kreidersville on the Lehigh. Beyond this line the Matinal formation of Trenton limestone and Hudson river slates stretches to the gray and reddish sandstones (IV.) of Blue mountain, which form its northern boundary. Brown hematite ore is abundant along the Lehigh, near the junction of the limestone with the primary rocks. In both Lehigh and Northampton counties the brown hematites in the Lower Silurian limestones and slates furnished the material for making iron as soon as anthracite proved available. The furnaces erected soon absorbed, as it was thought, the local production; but that has steadily increased as the soil has been more accurately explored. When the New Jersey magnetic ores were developed, the whole region rose to its present importance, for the Lehigh valley, commanding coal and brown hematite, needed only red-short magnetic ores to make the best iron. The New Jersey furnaces, on the other hand, needed the brown hematites, which exist in very limited quantities in that State. Hence freights were low, coal cheap through competition, and the favorable location opened the New York and eastern markets to the furnaces of the district.

In 1856 there were 4 anthracite-furnaces in the county. One at South Easton, 1845; 3 at Glendon, 1844, 1845, and 1850, built by Charles Jackson, Jr., of Boston. They were built for the brown hematites along the Lehigh river, and made, in 1856, 23,839 tons of pig iron. They have since used the New Jersey magnetic ores very largely, if not principally, and have, under Mr. William Firmstone, always been noted for the uniformity and quality of their forge iron. One rolling-mill (South Easton) made, in 1856, 1344 tons of iron, and 1 forge made 125 tons of blooms.

In 1873 there were in the county 15 anthracite-furnaces, which made 140,094 tons of pig iron; 1 rolling-mill, with a product of 1048 tons; 1 rail-mill, which produced 16,270 tons of rails, and a Bessemer-steel works, with 2 five-ton converters. This works went into operation October 4th, 1873. Its greatest product has been in one day, 264 gross tons; in a week, 1340 tons, and in a month, 5282 gross tons. Since August 4th, 1875, it has used spiegeleisen made at the works.

This works represents a third type of design.   It has its cupolas on the ground at some distance from the converting vessels, to the rear; the molten iron is collected at the cupolas in a ladle supported on a car which is pushed to the converting vessels by a small locomotive.   The spiegeleisen is melted in a Siemens' furnace, and transferred in the same way to the vessels. The converting arrangement consists of two vessels, side by side, as usual, and mounted with their chimneys on iron columns, as at Cambria; the tipping cylinder is bolted with its rack, and guides for the latter, to the iron beam supporting the outer trunnion of each vessel. In front, between the vessels, is a hydraulic hoist on to which the ladle-car runs, and is raised to the platform around the converters, where it pours its contents through short, semi-circular runners into either vessel. The dimensions of the plant are the usual ones, and it stands clear inside of a building large enough to accommodate a second similar plant.   The engines are horizontal, with poppet-valves, moved by cams on a shaft, at the side of and parallel with the cylinder, driven by bevel gearing from the main shaft.   Bell-crank levers lift the valves, which open directly into the cylinder at each end with the shortest possible passages.   From the pit the 4-rail ingots made are taken to Siemens' furnaces "to cool" and then rolled in a blooming-mill, the rolls in the tables of which are driven, in all positions, by a reversing engine, the power communicated by a splined shaft working through a bevel gear on the table.   The blooms are cut, reheated, and rolled as usual.

The blast-furnaces have brick stacks banded with iron, and the Player hot-ovens.   The small one uses Franklinite residuum in making spiegeleisen, and also New Jersey ores fit for the purpose.   The blowing-engines are the Fritz and Moore type, designed by Mr. James Moore from a pump built by Mr. John Fritz, at the Cambria works, and described with those works; the new furnaces will, however, have horizontal blowing-engines. The Bessemer works, the rail-mill, and a new large mill for steel rails and heavy beams (in operation 1874), as well as 5 large blast-furnaces (15 and 45, 15 and 50, 15 and 62, two 18 and 70 feet), and a small one for making spiegeleisen (10¾ and 31½ feet), belong to the Bethlehem Iron Company.

NORTHUMBERLAND COUNTY, formed in 1772 of part of Lancaster, Cumberland, Berks, Bedford, and Northampton. The formations of the county range from the Medina sandstones and Clinton shales (V.) of Montour's ridge to the coal measures. The county contains the eastern part of the Middle anthracite coal-field, including the Shamokin and Trevorton districts.

The Shamokin furnace, referred to under Lehigh county, was the first furnace in the county, and was built in 1842 for using anthracite, being located within a few hundred yards of the mouth of a coal-mine. Limestone was had within thirty yards of the stack. It was intended to carry a railroad to the tunnel-head, but it was preferred to raise the charges from the base of the furnace. For two proposed furnaces seven Calder stoves were built, three with 15, four with 20 pipes. It is an interesting fact that exchanges of coal for ore— ton for ton—were made by the Shamokin and the Danville companies. The Chulasky furnace was built in 1846, by Samuel Wood, of Philadelphia, one of the pioneers of American iron manufacture, and is still at work.

In 1856 there were in the county 1 charcoal-furnace (Paxinos, 1847), which made 350 tons in 1855, during its *last* blast; 2 anthracite-furnaces, those above described, of which the Shamokin made 2465 tons of pig iron, and 1 forge, with a product of say 250 tons.

In 1873 the county contained 1 anthracite-furnace (Chulasky), with a product of 4000 tons, and 2 rolling-mills, which made 3583 tons of bar iron, &c.

PERRY COUNTY, formed in 1820 of part of Cumberland. The geological formations of this county range from the Medina sandstones of the North and Tuscarora mountains to the red shales (XI.) underlying the conglomerate at the base of the coal measures in the extreme point of the south-western point of the southern anthracite coal-field, opposite Dauphin. Sandy and fossiliferous iron-ores are mined at various places, but are practically of little importance so far as developed.

This county has contributed very little to the history of iron-making, its mountainous surface and lean ores having discouraged enterprise, except in cases where water-power was very abundant. The Duncannon Rolling-mill, built in 1838, was for a long while the only iron-works in the county. In 1853 the Duncannon furnace was built.

In 1856 there was 1 anthracite-furnace (Duncannon), producing say 3000 tons, and the mill, which made 3850 tons of bar iron and nails.

In 1873 there were 2 anthracite-furnaces (the second Marshall, 1872), with a product of 8296 tons; 1 charcoal-furnace (Laura, 1873), which made 493 tons; a mill, which made 6242 tons; and 2 forges (Perry, 1862, was rebuilt 1872), which produced 1637 tons of blooms for boiler-plate.

PHILADELPHIA COUNTY, an original county of the province of Pennsylvania. It lies in the (White mountain) gneiss series of the primary formations, which are covered in the eastern and southern part of the county by a deep diluvial deposit.

It is a question whether Philadelphia had not one of the first forges in the province, namely, that called by Swedenborg John Ball, which may be the plating-forge of John Hall, in Bilberry township.

At even the earliest date, however, the iron-works moved toward the ore, and the industry at Philadelphia was confined to working up iron into tools and utensils. In 1750, as we have seen, Stephen Paschall was successful in making blister steel on a large scale, and William Branson had a steel-works in the city. Hall's plating-forge was then idle, but that did not matter much, as they were all suppressed as *common nuisances* in 1750. In 1770 Whithead Humphreys had a steel-works on Seventh street, between Market and Chestnut streets; he is the man afterward appointed by the Continental Congress to make steel out of Andover iron for the use of the army. Humphreys received aid in money from the Provincial Assembly and authority to raise £700 by a lottery, "so that he might make steel as good as the English." We find no mention of Paschall's forge till 1787, when it was again in operation, and belonged to Nancarrow and Matlack. One of these steel-works produced, according to a statement of Mr. Clymer, in Congress, 230 tons of steel yearly. There was also an air-furnace, belonging to Nancarrow, at the north-west corner of Ninth and Walnut streets, where he is said to have made some steel.

To illustrate the changes brought about by time, we find that in Philadelphia, in 1830, a convention "of the Iron Manufacturers of Philadelphia" petitioned Congress for the entire removal of duties on pig and scrap iron, boiler-plate, and loups, slabs, blooms, and other iron, except manufactured and bar iron; that all hammered bar iron be admitted at rate of April 27th, 1816, *i. e.*, 45 cents per cwt.; that all rolled iron and wire of iron and steel be admitted at 25 per cent.; that the duty on railroad iron be remitted, and the duties on steel abolished. This would have been a free-trade tariff, but was successfully opposed by a convention of Friends of Domestic Industry, held in *New York*, November, 1831, from whose report I have often quoted. They maintained it to be the right and the duty of Congress to impose duties for protection as well as for revenue. They succeeded in preventing any action till 1832, when was commenced a steady reduction of duties, ending in the uniform 20 per cent. *ad valorem* of 1842. It is needless to say that long before 1842 the "ironmasters of Philadelphia" had made a right-about face, and have ever since fully represented the domestic interests of the country as opposed to the import trade.

In 1833 Matthew Carey and Clem. C. Biddle reported to the Secretary of the Treasury that "J. & J. Rowland's mill was the only rolling and slitting mill in Philadelphia."

In 1856 the county contained 6 rolling-mills, the earliest of which was Flatrock (1820), with an estimated product of 4650 tons of boiler-plate, band, hoop, and bar iron; 1 mill (Treaty) was idle from 1853 to 1857; also, 5 steel-works, which made 2200 tons of cast and blister steel in all forms; they were the Kensington, 1840 and 1845; Oxford, 1855; Penn, 1845; and belonged to James Rowland & Co., J. Robbins, Earp & Brink, Robert S. Johnson, and W. & H. Rowland.

In 1873 there was 1 anthracite-furnace (Robbins, 1873), which made in 1873 400 tons of pig iron after getting into blast; 9 rolling-mills, with a product of 47,301 tons, and 6 cast-steel works, which made 5810 tons.

SCHUYLKILL COUNTY, formed in 1811 of parts of Berks and Northampton. The formations rise from the Clinton red shales (V.) through the anthracite coal measures. It contains two great basins—the Southern and Middle basins, as well as parts of the Beaver Meadow, Green mountain, Tomhicken, and Black creek basins. The fossil ore has no workable outcrops in the county, and though the black-band carbonates have been worked near Pottsville, yet they are unreliable and unimportant so far as known.

Anthracite coal was known in the Wyoming valley in 1768, when the proprietaries bought their western lands from the Six Nations. In 1770 Erskine Hazard said it was tested by blacksmiths three years before Wilkesbarre was laid out by the Susquehanna Land Company of Connecticut. The first cargo was sent down the Susquehanna in 1775 to the United States armory at Carlisle. In the Schuylkill region, coal was known near Pottsville before 1770, for on a map of Pennsylvania, of 1770, from Scull's older map, coal is marked about the headwaters of "Schuylkill creek," and thence westward to the Swatara and to "the wilderness of Saint Anthony." The Summit mine, near Mauch Chunk, was discovered 1791, and the "Lehigh Coal Mine Company" formed in 1793. The first anthracite found its way from Pottsville to Philadelphia in 1812, and from Mauch Chunk in 1814; the first coal in the Philadelphia market appeared in 1820, and the first bituminous coal reached tide-water from Clearfield, as we have seen, in 1804.

In 1820 the county was "almost a wilderness of

unseated lands" (Shunk); but the *Mining Journal* records, in 1828, 1 furnace (Greenwood), which belonged to John & Benjamin Potts, and used ore brought by canal from Reading and Pottsgrove; 4 forges in operation (Schuylkill, 1801, being the first), and 2 forges being built. The 4 forges made 500 tons of bar iron, and the furnace made " 20 tons a week." Bar iron was worth $100 per ton at the forge, and charcoal pig iron $28 at the furnace.

In 1834 there were in the county, according to a report to the Secretary of the Treasury, 3 charcoal-furnaces, making 1750 tons of pig iron and 550 tons of castings yearly, and 7 forges, with a product of 1150 tons of bar iron.

In 1840 there were 4 furnaces, 6 forges, and a rolling-mill. The Pottsville furnace was completed in January of this year by Mr. Lyman. It was the second to use anthracite successfully, but the first to make a *three months' continuous blast,* for which it took a prize, under general congratulations. A second anthracite-furnace, near Pottsville, called the Schuylkill Valley furnace, built by Dr. F. W. Geisenheimer, was blown in on September 17th, 1841, and "worked finely from the start on the ores of the anthracite beds."

While all these efforts were being made to smelt with anthracite, some attention was devoted to its qualities for other purposes. The *Miners' Journal*, in December, 1834, published a letter, stating that M. B. Buckley, of Pottsville, had puddled iron with anthracite into metal of excellent quality, at a cost of from $10 to $15 less than by the usual methods. On this *Hazard's Register* remarked that, since Buckley had discovered puddling with anthracite, the only thing needed was the discovery of some means of smelting with anthracite.

This brought out a correspondent from Phœnixville, who wrote "that at least 27 tons were puddled with anthracite at Phœnixville in 1827, and part of it made into boiler iron. The fact was well known to many gentlemen of Philadelphia, but they knew that bituminous was as abundant as anthracite coal, which could never supersede the use of bituminous coal."

The first regular shipment of anthracite from Schuylkill county was in 1825, amounting to 5306 tons; the quantity increased to 89,984 tons in 1830, to 335,685 tons in 1835, and to 584,692 tons in 1841, exclusive of 20,000 tons used in the county. This shows that when the experiments took place with anthracite, in the blast-furnace, it was both plentiful and cheap, compared with other fuels.

In 1856 2 anthracite-furnaces made 4874 tons of pig iron; 2 forges made 200 tons of blooms; 1 rolling-mill (Palo Alto) produced 1500 tons, and 2 rail-mills (Pottsville 3021 tons, Palo Alto 1000 tons) made 4021 tons of rails.

In 1873 there were in the county 8 anthracite-furnaces, with a product of 48,612 tons of pig iron; 1 charcoal-furnace, which made 1103 tons; 4 rolling-mills, which produced 2535 tons; 2 rail-mills, which made 23,765 tons of iron rails, and one forge.

SNYDER COUNTY, formed in 1855 of part of Union. This county had in 1856 1 charcoal-furnace, the Beaver, built in 1848, which lay in Middle Creek valley, on the north side of Shade mountain. In 1857 it made 1030 tons of pig iron. The ores it used were fossil ores from Clinton (V.) outcrops along the foot of Shade mountain, like those from Montour's ridge, near Danville. This furnace was abandoned, and in 1873 there were no iron-works in the county.

SOMERSET COUNTY, formed in 1795 of part of Bedford. Nearly the whole of this county lies in the bituminous-coal formation of the First basin, while a bed of limestone occurs in many places just below the conglomerate at the foot of the coal measures, and others between the coal-beds. Coal-measure ores are also found along the east side of Laurel Hill and were mined at the head of Carey's run for the old Fayette furnace on Indian creek. Considerable amounts were mined on Shade, Wells, and Stony creeks.

The earliest furnace was the Shade furnace, which was built, with its forge, in 1812 and abandoned in 1855. In 1840 this furnace and forge were the only ones in operation in the county, the forge making yearly 20 tons of bar iron. In 1843 the Rockingham charcoal-furnace was built (abandoned 1856), the Somerset charcoal-furnace was built in 1846 (idle from 1848 to 1856), and the Wellersburg furnace in 1856.

In 1856 the Wellersburg and Somerset furnaces made 1447 tons of pig iron, and the forge had been abandoned.

In 1873 there were no iron-works in operation in the county.

TIOGA COUNTY, formed in 1804 of part of Lycoming. This county lies in the formations of the Chemung and Portage groups, partly covered to the west by the conglomerate below the coal formations. At Blossburg there is a basin belonging to the lower coal measures. The deep cuts of the streams have exposed iron-ore of the Umbral red shales (XI.) in four thin seams in shales and fire-clay. Above the lowest coal-vein a bed of kidney carbonate ore in shale is sometimes over a foot thick; but the total development of iron-ore, so far as known, is inconsiderable.

The iron manufacture of the county has been unimportant. One furnace at Blossburg was built in 1841 for charcoal, but altered for coke. It was erected mainly by G. J. Boyd, a bank cashier of Blossburg, and was for a while in successful operation. But Boyd was immoral, defaulted very extensively, and shot himself. On this the furnace was allowed to chill through on its first blast, and has done nothing since.

In 1856 this furnace was in ruins, but 1 rolling-mill (Blossburg) made 322 tons of bar, and the Mansfield charcoal-furnace made 600 tons of pig iron.

In 1871 the Mansfield furnace was altered for anthracite, and made 3850 tons, and is now consolidated with the Blossburg mill as the Tioga Iron-works.

UNION COUNTY, formed in 1813 of part of Northumberland. The formations of this county range from the Medina sandstones (IV.) to the top of the Devonian Chemung (VIII.) and Catskill (IX.), in the Blue Hill, on the southern line, in red and gray sandstones and shales. The fossil iron-ore of Montour's ridge is prolonged into Union county along the West Branch of the Susquehanna, but thins out so as to be of comparatively little value on Penn's creek, in Jack's Mountain Gap. The Medina sandstone, in its ridges along the western side of the county, seems to have no valuable outcrop of its ore. In 1827 the first furnace (Berlin, 6 and 32 feet) was built at Berlin, the next in 1846 (Forrest).

In 1856 these two made about 1942 tons of pig iron, and 1 anthracite-furnace (Union, 1854) made 3600 tons out of Cornwall magnetic and Danville red fossil ores.

In 1873 the Union furnace was the only works left, and it made 4621 tons of pig iron. In 1875, however, the old Forrest had been repaired and started again by M. A. Pardee as the White Deer Charcoal-furnace.

VENANGO COUNTY, formed in 1800 of parts of Allegheny and Lycoming. Venango lies on the northern border of the coal formations and partly in the measures just below them. There is coal in the southern part of the county, and nodular carbonate and bog ores occur in some quantity and in similar positions to those in which they occur in Clarion county. The iron manufacture has always been based on charcoal.

In 1828 the county made about 1600 tons of pig iron, 200 tons of blooms, and 100 tons of bar iron. The pig was sent to Pittsburg, Steubenville, and Wheeling, where it sold at $35 to $40 per ton and the blooms at $100, while the bar iron sold at Franklin at $125 to $140 per ton. Of the furnaces of that day it was said, "With proper management a furnace will make 800 to 1000 tons per annum, at a cost of $22 to $24 per ton, according to price of provisions. With ore and wood convenient and good the cost would be $18 to $20. Under proper management, with good materials, a profit of $10,000 should be yearly made."

In 1831 there were in the county 4 furnaces, 1 bloomery, and 2 forges.

In 1843 17 charcoal-furnaces were in operation in the county, and between 1830 and 1853 27 were erected in all. Fifteen of them were abandoned before 1853 and 4 in 1856. The history of these furnaces is exactly like those in the adjacent county, Clarion. They were usually built on streams affording water-power, and wherever ore enough was found, but the leanness of the ore and the long distance from market made it impossible for them to compete with the coke-furnaces nearer market, even for special purposes.

In 1856 there were 9 furnaces in the county, with a product of 5830 tons, and in 1874 they had all been abandoned, and the progress of the trade had obliterated another iron district. The oil production of the county absorbed all its energies and consoled its citizens for the loss of their iron trade.

WESTMORELAND COUNTY, formed in 1773 of part of Bedford. It lies wholly in the great bituminous coal formations of the Third and Fourth basins; several strata of limestone occur between the coal-beds, and coal-measure carbonates have been mined in many places, especially along the base of Laurel Hill.

Iron-making was commenced on account of the impetus given by the passage through the county of the great western highways, which were finally established as the National road to Wheeling and the Northern and Southern roads from Pittsburg to Philadelphia.

The *Universal Asylum*, quoted by Ebeling in 1797 in his history of Pennsylvania, states that "*Jacob's furnace and forge in Westmoreland county were both built in 1790 by J. Turnbull, and were the first west of the mountains.*" And Ebeling mentions another works—a forge. The furnace we believe to be that of Turnbull & Marmie, in Fayette county, already mentioned, but the furnace lay on the boundary between the counties.

In 1840 there were 4 or 5 charcoal-furnaces in the county. In 1856 there were 2 charcoal-furnaces (California, 1852; Oak Grove, 1854), with a product of 834 tons; 1 coke-furnace (Valley C., 1855), which made 500 tons, at the rate of 50 tons per week. The Laurel furnace, built in 1846, was abandoned in 1856.

In 1873 there was only one works in the county,—a coke-furnace, the Charlotte, built in 1873, which made 2200 tons of pig iron.

YORK COUNTY, formed in 1749 of part of Lancaster. It lies principally in the primary metamorphic formations, crossed in the south by belts of serpentine, and in the north overlaid by new Red Strata, which are broken by extensive dykes and hills of trap. The primary and new red formations are separated by a wide belt of Lower Silurian limestone, extending across the county from Wrightsville to the Pigeon hills, and drained principally by the Codorus creek. Brown hematite occurs richly in the limestone belts and specular ore in the Pigeon hills; around York a peculiar specular, partly magnetic ore occurs in pots in clay, while very pure magnetic ore is mined somewhat in the northern part, in the neighborhood of the trap at Dillsburg and elsewhere.

The earliest mention of iron-works in this county is that of Acrelius, who records, in 1759, Dixon's Works, in York county, and mentions that it was a bloomery. In 1797 Ebeling reports 1 furnace, the Mary Ann, on Codorus creek, and below it the Spring and Hallam forges, which made 300 tons of bar iron yearly.

In 1830 the only works in operation were 3 forges,—Codorus, Spring, and Castlefin, which made 850 tons of bar iron. These forges, as well as the earlier ones, worked brown hematite ores.

In 1843 there were 4 furnaces and 4 forges in the county.

In 1856 1 charcoal-furnace (York, 1830) made 1000 tons, and 2 forges (Castlefin, 1810; Woodstock, 1828) made 1100 tons of blooms and 100 tons of bar iron. The Castlefin Works included a steel-works, which made 100 tons of blister steel yearly.

In 1874 there were in the county 1 anthracite-furnace (Aurora, 1867), which made 6150 tons of pig iron; 1 charcoal-furnace (York), 1 rolling-mill (Codorus Steel-works, 1869), with a product of 448 tons; and a forge (Castlefin) which made 400 tons of blooms.

The Codorus mill, though young, has a history,—the common one in cases where experience in iron manufacture is sought to be reversed by startling discoveries. The invention of the use of Codorus ore, a lean, silicious specular ore, was described in the New York *Tribune* as the use of an ore " which, though it makes of itself but 40 per cent. of poor (pig) iron, yet, being mixed with very common pig iron in an ordinary reverberatory furnace, in the proportion of one to five, produces at low cost choice steel, well adapted to any use which steel has hitherto subserved." It is needless to say this has not been the case. The ore, highly silicious, caused waste of pig iron in the puddling-furnace, and hence a thin slag, which hindered oxidation, and made a *puddled steel* with all the defects of that material. The principal use to which the product has been put is for rail-heads at the Elmira Rolling-mill. The silicious cinder, while it wasted the iron, did not remove impurities.

The reputation of Pennsylvania as an iron-producing State, as has been fittingly said, " has resulted more from the energetic, persevering German use for a century of years of what ores do exist than from any extraordinary wealth of iron (ores) of which she can boast." The history of her iron trade has a continuous record of nearly one hundred and fifty years, and the progress made, though slow, has been effectual. Her metallurgy differs from that of all other States in that, from the very beginning, she has scarcely used the bloomery fire, and that her operations have, therefore, in the earlier periods been on a larger scale, more complicated, but more economical than the operations of her sister States. In the course of time we find, as has been described, the essential improvements of to-day first introduced or originated at her various works,—and we have thus followed the history of *iron manufacture* in the United States as well. We have seen how, partly from natural causes, partly in manufacture, one district after another has lost its hold on the supremacy, or, like Clarion and Venango counties, given up the manufacture altogether.

The spectacle has a double significance. So far as the individual manufacturer is concerned, his works should be located where they command the most extensive connections and the cheapest fuel and ores of the desired quality. It must be borne in mind that always as phase has succeeded phase—through cold-short iron, then red-short, when quicker rolling enabled such iron to be worked, then " neutral " iron, in which red-shortness and cold-shortness are both present—the tendency has been to demand stronger metal more and more free from phosphorus. We have never made purely cinder iron in this country; it is to be hoped we never shall, unless it be deprived of phosphorus in some way. So far as the State is concerned the obvious duty of protection and such encouragement as shall develop its own resources to the utmost is impressed in the plainest signs on every page of our history. Mining, manufacturing, and transportation companies support the State (almost literally in Pennsylvania, as they pay nearly all the State taxes), and should be intelligently governed and encouraged. The early growth of the anthracite iron manufacture was due to legislative encouragement, while the benefit arising from the first State geological survey is incalculable. The usefulness of the second geological survey will be still greater, for our people are now in a position to utilize discoveries and exact knowledge, while they formerly did not know in what direction to develop the resources of the State.

The possession of mineral fuel is, doubtless, a great advantage; but no productive iron-ore mines are found in the coal measures, and by the supposed necessities of transportation other States share the advantage of cheap fuel on nearly equal terms with Pennsylvania, so far as anthracite is concerned. The ultimate effect of such a policy, if seriously pursued, will, of course, be to transfer the principal iron-producing districts to the regions richest in ore or to localities possessing both coal and ore—in either case to prepare a new situation in the ceaseless round.

The start of our iron trade was made between 1836 and 1840. The Lehigh navigation had been opened in 1820 for traffic and the Mauch Chunk Railroad built in 1827; the Union canal in 1824, of which the first surveys had been made in 1762; the Schuylkill canal was fairly in use in 1826, and the great Pennsylvania canal, with its Portage and Columbia auxiliary railroads, carried traffic in 1834, and before 1840 had a through connection, by the Beaver river and Ohio canal, to Cleveland on Lake Erie. The Reading Railroad was finished in 1838, and in 1840 the State contained 974 miles of canal and 953½ of railroad lines open for use. The means of transport were thus, for that time, amply provided, and from that time furnaces and rolling-mills deserted the streams that facilitated transportation, but too often furnished a delusive show of power. Then, also, our forges ceased to make bar iron, and practically turned that work over to rolling-mills fitted for the purpose.

In 1836 an act was passed authorizing the governor to form corporations for making iron with coke or mineral fuel on exceedingly favorable terms. In 1836 coke and in 1838 anthracite were used as furnace fuel. In 1836 furnace gases were first used, and in 1838 the hot blast was applied. The production of charcoal pig has diminished most rapidly ever since and with unvarying regularity; we shall, doubtless, soon be like England with her *two* charcoal-furnaces.

We scarcely think nowadays how much of our progress is due to the " Society for the Promotion of Internal Improvement in the Commonwealth of Pennsylvania," of which John Sergeant, Matthew Carey, Thomas Biddle, Richard Peters, Jr., Josiah Randall, John White, Levett Harris, Abraham Shoemaker, and Gerard Ralston were the representatives in 1826. The Convention on Internal Improvement, held at Harrisburg in 1825, took the first steps to place the State where it now stands, by urging on the legislature the necessity " of an entire and complete communication from the Susquehanna to the Allegheny and Ohio and from the Allegheny to Lake Erie." The society made in 1825 the first suggestion of a geological survey, and sent Mr. Strickland, in 1825, with his whilom pupil, Mr. Kneass, to England, to report on canals, railways, roads and bridges, breakwaters, gas-lights, and the manufacture of iron. Their reports now read somewhat like the practical discussions of Miss Edgeworth's " Harry and Lucy." Their tenor reminds us strongly that half a century is a short period in which to achieve so much.

The policy of internal improvement thus begun in 1826, "to maintain the character and standing of the State and to preserve her strength and resources," bore immediate fruit in the growth of the iron trade between 1830 and 1842. The early works lay on the Schuylkill, the Susquehanna, the Allegheny, and the

Youghiogheny rivers, and those in Centre, Huntingdon, and Mifflin, formerly the most important iron district in the State, were built up by the Pennsylvania canal. This canal, at the time of its building, reached, with the Union canal and the western extensions, nearly every important district in the State. They found works ready to use its facilities; hence the rapid strides made by the early iron production. The Pennsylvania Railroad, the Reading and the Lehigh Valley Railroads, and their systems have now taken the place of the canal system, and hold an equally important place with reference to the works of to-day. Cheap and regular transportation is, as we have seen, the life of the iron trade, and with that stimulus the districts already noted for their early enterprise will develop a strength and capacity unexpected to the most sanguine hopes.

Statistics of the Iron Trade of Pennsylvania from the Earliest Times.

1730.

4 furnaces (Logan, 1728), estimated, . .	1,072 tons pig iron.
9 forges and 2 bloomeries (Swedenborg, 1734), estimated, ...	300 tons bar iron.

1751.

6 furnaces, estimated, ...	2,500 tons pig iron.
7 forges (Governor Denny), official, . . .	526 $\frac{888}{2240}$ tons bar iron.

1759.

12 furnaces (Acrelius), estimated, · . . .	5,000 tons pig iron.
12 forges and 1 bloomery (Acrelius), estimated, ... ·	975 tons bar iron.

1780.

17 furnaces (Hasenclever), estimated, . .	6,000 tons pig iron.
25 forges (Hasenclever), estimated, . . .	2,700 tons bar iron.
2 steel-works (blister), estimated, ...	150 tons steel.

1789.

14 furnaces (Potts), Potts, ... {	5,150 tons pig iron. 1,000 tons castings.
34 forges (Potts), Potts, ...	3,600 tons bar iron.

1797.

16 furnaces, { in operation (Ebeling), esti- {	7,500 tons pig iron.
37 forges, { mated, ... {	4,200 tons bar iron.

"Between 1788 and 1794 half as many works were started as there were works before 1788." (Coxe, View.)

1820.

Mitchell, ...	21,350 tons bar iron.

1827.

Mitchell, ... {	47,075 tons pig iron. 21,800 tons bar iron.

"As many forges in 1820 as in 1828, and 450 tons more bar (iron) made in 1827 than in 1820." (Mitchell.)

1828.

44 furnaces (Co. Pa. House Rep.), . . . {	24,822 tons pig iron. 3,693 tons castings.
78 forges and rolling-mills (French), . .	Under-estimated.

1829.

44 furnaces (Co. Pa. House Rep.), . . . $\left\{\begin{array}{l}\text{27,425 tons pig iron.}\\ \text{4,564 tons castings.}\end{array}\right.$

84 forges and rolling-mills (French), . . Under-estimated.

1830.

45 furnaces (Co. Pa. House Rep.), . . . $\left\{\begin{array}{l}\text{31,056 tons pig iron.}\\ \text{5,706 tons castings.}\\ \text{Under-estimated.}\end{array}\right.$

1839

(Returns of County Commissioners in Pa.
Senate Journal; also, Hunt's Merch. Mag.,
MacGregor, Chambers.)

213 furnaces (French's, 151,885 tons, grossly $\left.\begin{array}{l}\\ \end{array}\right\}$ 190,000 tons pig iron.
incorrect), ...

145 forges, rolling-mills, nail-works, &c., . $\left\{\begin{array}{l}\text{120,300 tons bar iron, plate,}\\ \text{blooms, &c.}\end{array}\right.$

There were 506,724 tons of ore mined in
the State to produce the 190,000 tons product, estimated from actual returns of 699
townships. The ore yielded 37½ per cent.,
or one ton of pig iron to 2⅔ tons of ore.

1841.

230 furnaces (Philadelphia Committee), . . 194,580 tons.

(Of these 12 were anthracite-furnaces,
making 15,000 tons (H. K. Strong, 1842)
and 1 coke-furnace (Karthaus') not in
operation).

160 forges, rolling-mills, and nail-works, . . 70,040 tons.

1847.

	1847.		1849.	
57 anthracite-furnaces, . .	151,331	tons pig iron.	109,168	tons pig iron.
7 raw-coal "	7,800	" "	4,900	" "
4 coke "	10,000	" "	. . . .	
230 charcoal " $\left.\right)$				
85 hot-blast, . . . $\left.\right\}$	94,519	" "	58,302	" "
145 cold-blast, . . $\left.\right)$	125,155	" "	70,727	" "
121 forges (402 fires), . .	39,997	" blooms.	28,495	" blooms.
6 bloomeries, ...	545	" "	335	" "
78 rolling-mills, . . . $\left\{\right.$	122,764	" bar, plate, &c.	89,385	" bar, plate, &c.
6 rail-mills, ...	40,996	" rails.	18,973	" rails.

13 steel-works (blister and cast), 6078 tons steel (1847). (Philadelphia
Convention Iron-masters, 1849.)

1856.

93 anthracite-furnaces, ...	306,972 tons pig iron.
6 raw-coal furnaces, ...	8,417 tons pig iron.
21 coke-furnaces, ...	39,953 tons pig iron.
143 charcoal-furnaces, ...	96,154 tons pig iron.
111 forges, ...	31,727 tons blooms and bar.
93 rolling-mills, ...	156,650 tons bar, plate, &c.
8 rail-mills (also, a mill tolling 1000 tons),	84,834 tons rails.

6 steel-works in operation (capacity 8500). (?)

1864.

105 anthracite-furnaces (90 in blast), . . .	519,600 tons pig iron.
20 coke-furnaces, ...	77,549 tons pig iron.
17 raw-coal furnaces (11 in blast), ...	44,671 tons pig iron.
70 charcoal-furnaces (61 in blast), ...	53,171 tons pig iron.
71 forges (67 in operation), ...	34,911 tons blooms, &c.
93 rolling-mills, ...	232,714 tons bar, plate, &c.
11 rail-mills, ...	157,722 tons rails.
14 steel-works (one-quarter cast, three-quarters blister), ...	9,771 tons steel.

1873.

149 anthracite-furnaces, ...	913,085 tons pig iron.
25 raw-coal furnaces, ...	160,831 tons pig iron.
49 coke-furnaces, ...	269,803 tons pig iron.
39 charcoal-furnaces, ...	45,854 tons pig iron.
33 forges, ...	23,748 tons blooms.
121 rolling-mills, ...	480,469 tons bar, plate, &c.
17 rail-mills, ...	328,522 tons iron rails.
16 cast-steel works, ...	33,151 tons cast steel.
4 Bessemer-steel works (2 building), . .	47,533 tons steel rails, &c.

In the entire country the production of Bessemer steel rails has been: —

In 1867, ... 2,550 net tons.	In 1872, ... 94,070 net tons.
1868, ... 7,225 "	1873, ... 129,015 "
1869, ... 9,650 "	1874, ... 144,944 "
1870, ... 34,000 "	1875, ... 290,863 "
1871, ... 38,250 "	

The production of the Pennsylvania works has increased since 1873 in the same proportion.

Production of Pig Iron with Mineral Fuel in Pennsylvania in Net Tons after 1865.

Before 1865, *gross tons.* Net ton was adopted as unit in 1865 by American Iron and Steel Association.

DISTRICT.	1849.	1854.	1860.	1864.	1872.	1875.
Lehigh, anthracite............	44,347	92,323	173,075	214,093	449,663	280,360
Schuylkill, "	23,436	62,570	92,345	112,806	232,225	123,184
Lower Susquehanna, anthracite......	24,256	72,040	101,246	118,615	159,305½	79,717
Upper Susquehanna, "	26,625	65,332	66,698	106,964	127,259½	71,731
Shenango, raw coal............	....	10,100	17,764	44,671	160,188	137,025
Western Pennsylvania, coke........	....	19,841	51,984	77,549	227,823	234,376
Total, Pennsylvania............	....	322,206	503,112	674,698	1,356,464	926,393
Total, United States............	650,000	724,833	884,474	1,145,497	2,854,558	2,266,581

Production of Pig Iron in the United States (in gross tons, 2240 pounds). Compiled by J. B. Pearse. Believed to be correct.

1810.	53,908¾	Tench Coxe for A. Gallatin, Secretary Treasury.
1828.	123,404	Philadelphia Convention, 1831.
1829.	134,954	Philadelphia Convention, 1831.
1830.	180,598	Philadelphia Convention; corrected 1831 by Peter Townsend.
1831.	191,536	New York Convention; H. C. Carey, R. C. Taylor.
1832.	200,000	Carey.
1832 to 1839 no extension; Thomas Chambers.		
1837.	250,000	Lea; *incorrect*, J. H. Alexander.
1839.	235,000	Alexander.
1840.	317,306	average { 347,700 Home League, N. Y. / 286,903 U. S. Census.
1842.	215,000	J. D. Whitney; over 200,000 under 230,000, H. C. Carey.
1844.	486,000	Home League, N. Y.
1845.	502,000	Whitney.
1846.	765,000	estimate of Secretary of Treasury Walker.
1847.	800,000	estimate of Secretary of Treasury Walker; over 500,000 tons, Feuchtwanger.
1848.	800,000	Carey.
1849.	650,000	Carey; *correct*, Abram S. Hewitt.
1850.	563,755	U. S. Census; 400,000 tons, S. S. Haldeman.
1851.	413,000	B. F. French.
1852.	540,755	French.
1853.	805,000	(?). Estimate quoted by French.
1854.	724,833	J. P. Lesley and Chas. E. Smith for Am. Iron Ass'n.
1855.	728,973	Lesley, &c.
1856.	812,917	Lesley, &c.
1857.	798,157	American Iron Association.
1858.	705,094	American Iron Association.
1859.	840,627	American Iron Association.
1860.	884,474	U. S. Census.
1861.	731,544	American Iron Association.
1862.	787,662	American Iron Association.
1863.	947,604	American Iron Association.
1864.	1,145,497	Dunlap, secretary National Ass'n Iron Manufacturers.
1865.	823,831	Calculation from net tons Am. Iron and Steel Ass'n.
1866.	1,205,041	Calculation from net tons Am. Iron and Steel Ass'n.
1867.	1,303,769	Calculation from net tons Am. Iron and Steel Ass'n.
1868.	1,429,876	Calculation from net tons Am. Iron and Steel Ass'n.
1869.	1,709,643	Calculation from net tons Am. Iron and Steel Ass'n.
1870.	1,663,580	Calculation from net tons Am. Iron and Steel Ass'n.
1871.	1,706,046	Calculation from net tons Am. Iron and Steel Ass'n.
1872.	2,546,265	Calculation from net tons Am. Iron and Steel Ass'n.
1873.	2,558,503	Calculation from net tons Am. Iron and Steel Ass'n.
1874.	2,398,956	Calculation from net tons Am. Iron and Steel Ass'n.
1875.	2,021,990	Calculation from net tons Am. Iron and Steel Ass'n

ACKNOWLEDGMENTS.

I gratefully acknowledge the aid I have received from the following gentlemen:—P. W. Sheafer, for use of map of Pennsylvania, which I have merely brought up to date; F. C. Lowthrop, for tracing of Mauch Chunk furnace; Barnum, Richardson & Co., for Lakeville furnace lines; C. E. Detmold and Alexander Campbell, Solomon Roberts, Charles Huston, Joshua Hunt; G. A. Berry, and James Veech, for information concerning Western furnaces; Paris Haldeman, S. M. Felton, D. J. Morrell, William E. Coffin, Abram S. Hewitt, George H. Cook, E. B. Coxe, J. D. Weeks, E. C. Pechin, Lucy and Isabella Furnace Companies; Spencer Bonsal, and the Historical Society of Pennsylvania; the librarians of the Philadelphia, American Philosophical Society, German Society, Franklin Institute, and Mercantile, of Philadelphia, of the Congressional Library, the Harvard College and Boston Public Library, and of the State Library at Harrisburg; specially to George R. Howell and State Library at Albany; James M. Swank, for statistics of the iron trade since 1870, and many other gentlemen who have willingly assisted me.

Also, among many others, the following books:—

Hazard's Gazetteer, Niles' Register, Harris' Pittsburg Directory, Franklin Institute Journal, Transactions Royal Society, Memoirs American Academy Science, Publications American Iron Association and of American Iron and Steel Association, Fisher's Industrial Record, Lesley's Iron Manufacturers' Guide, Statistics Iron Manufacture in Pennsylvania, Johnson's Iron with Anthracite, Johnson's (Franklin Institute) Strength of Materials, Taylor's Statistics of Coal, Overman on Iron, Alexander on Iron, Percy on Iron, *Karsten Eisenhüttenkunde*, Swedenborg's *Regnum Subterraneum*, Mehrbach's *Anw. d. erhitzten Gebläseluft*, Mushet on Iron and Steel, Scrivenor's History Iron Trade; Coal, Iron, and Oil, Daddow & Bannan; Whitney's Metallic Wealth of the United States, Macgregor's Progress of America, Tench Coxe's View of United States, Potts' Memorial, Penn Manuscripts, Peter Force's American Reprints, Kalm's Travels in America, Acrelius' History of New Sweden, Gee's Trade and Navigation of Great Britain, Ebeling's Collection of Maps (Harvard), Ebeling's History United States, Neill's Virginia Colony, Beverly's History Virginia, Keith's History Virginia, Williams' Virginia, Pennsylvania Colonial Records, Pennsylvania Archives, Budd's Good Order in Pennsylvania and New Jersey, Day's Historical Collections, Western Annals, Byrd's Westover Manuscripts, New York Documentary History, Collections Massachusetts and other Historical Societies, Lewis & Newhall's History of Lynn, Annals of Lynn, Hutchinson Papers, Records of Plymouth Colony and of Massachusetts Bay, New York Tribune, American Railroad Journal, all accessible State and County Histories and Gazetteers; Rogers' Geology of Pennsylvania; Reports and Papers of Messrs. J. T. Hodge, J. P. Lesley, C. M. Wetherill, &c., &c.

INDEX.